"Mike has done it again! **Return to the River** picks up where **Give Me the Hudson or the Yukon** left off. Bright and full of warmth, his unique insights float us down the river of life, from tears to waves of laughter. Once again he has put together a diverse collection of stories touched by wit and humor that is inspired by his friendships.

If you want to feel elated, to smile, to sometimes enjoy the ridiculous side of life, then read these stories."

Sharon Nault,
Field Editor, The Milepost ®
1973-1984

"Mike McCann captures the essence of life in the Alaskan bush. These are the stories Alaskans tell each other when the fire is going good in the stove and dinner is over, dogs are doing the dishes and the homebrew is almost ripe. They are ordinary stories about friends and neighbors, about defrosting 800 pounds of chicken liver in the back of the car at minus 50 degrees, about people being unprepared for winter and being rescued, about the dogs we loved, about the funny things that happen to people's minds when they live in isolation, about getting around the country in small planes, and really about all the unusual ways people find to survive and enjoy themselves immensely while doing it. Mike's stories make me want to move back to the Bush!"

Denise Lassaw,
Poet, Story Teller, Adventurer

"Mother-In-Law" appeared in *Alaska* magazine, November 1994.

"Bigger Boom" appeared in *Alaska* magazine, May 1995.

Printed and bound in the USA.
ISBN 0-9627530-1-7

Published by:
Ridgetop Press
P.O. Box 1521
Homer, AK 99603
(907) 235-5313

A special thanks to the Homer Writers' Group, Linda Feiler, Shirley Timmreck, Camille Whitmire, Susan Wohlgemuth, and Barb McNinch for their time and encouragement. Thanks also to David Hulen, Anchorage Daily News, for his contribution to the story "Alex."

Cover Photo: Stan Zuray, Charlie Campbell, Mike McCann (author), and Alex Tarnai at the confluence of the Yukon and Tanana rivers, March 1995

RETURN
to the
IVER

Another Collection of *Mostly True Stories*
from the Hudson and the Yukon

by Mike McCann

❖

Ridgetop Press
P.O. Box 1521
Homer, Alaska 99603
(907) 235-5313

Contents

Part I
From the Yukon River, Tanana, Alaska

Part II
Over the Tundra

Part III
Back on the Hudson

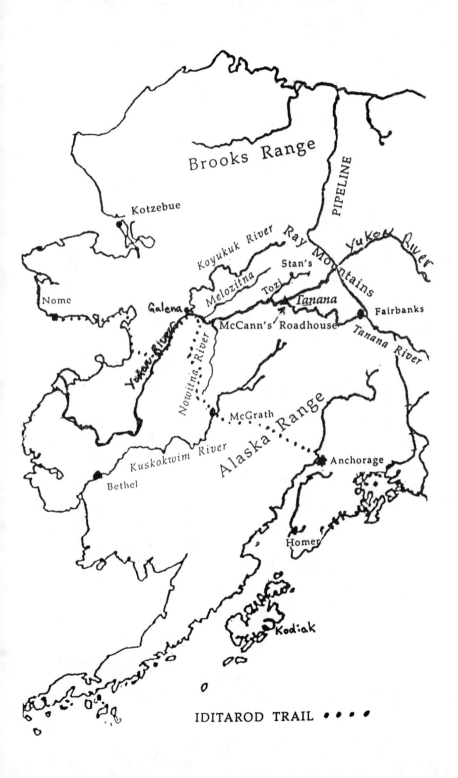

Part I

From the Yukon River
Tanana, Alaska

Lee

I met Lee my first night on the job at the Bush hospital in Tanana on the Yukon River. He had a tube down his nose and an intravenous line taped to his thin, veined arm. I introduced myself to this shriveled man. He reached out from under the cover with a big, bony hand and nodded slightly. His skin was yellow, cheeks sunken; he looked a goner to me.

There were few patients, so I had time to return and read his chart thoroughly. Lee had just had stomach surgery. It didn't look good for the 70-year-old man, according to the surgeon's report.

When I made rounds at 2 a.m., I checked for a pulse. Lee was awake, and I could see his lips moving in the dim light. I slid a chair over and sat close to the bed rail. In the dark Lee talked in a clear whisper. There was a big Eskimo man snoring across the dorm room. Lee said, "I sure appreciate you people taking care of me."

I didn't know what to say. The little man talked and kept me spellbound, telling how he had lived on the Yukon all his life and seen many people come and go. The more he talked the wider his smile grew and the fonder the memories seemed to get.

"Get a dog team. That's the way to see this country," Lee told me, "Then build a small fishwheel to feed you and your dogs." He sat up and hunched forward, spreading his arms out and said with a questioning look, "What else do you need?"

I envied his simple approach and laughed along with him when he shared his mishaps and adventures.

Lee said that when he was young his family was so poor they took 22-caliber bullets and replaced the lead tips with small nails. He explained how he would stalk a rabbit until it stopped in front of a tree. Then he would shoot the rabbit through the ears with the nail and pin him to the tree. That way he saved the skin, the meat and the bullet. He grinned.

When he was old enough to hunt black bears, Lee's mother told him not to shoot the hide full of holes. He was told to shoot the escaping bear in the butt, then quickly lay flat on the ground. She warned him that the angry bear would spin around so fast he might get shot with the bullet when it came out of the bear's mouth.

Back at the nurses' station, I told Julie, the older Eskimo nurse, "Old Lee is talking up a storm."

She said, "He loves to tell stories. He's like a grandfather to everyone in the village, but he sure looks bad this time." She sadly shook her head.

That morning Lee could only stand with help. His body was a skeleton draped with skin, bent over like a willow branch. I hooked arms and supported his eighty pounds while we shuffled down the hall. Halfway back to the room Lee stopped, caught his breath and looking serious, commented, "This is the first time I walked arm-in-arm with a guy." I burst out laughing; he had me. I hoped and prayed he made it through this bout. I knew we could be friends.

Six years later Lee stood up—as my best man.

What's Its Name?

I am amazed at how much trouble some parents have picking a name for their newborn. While working in hospitals I've seen many couples bring in books of name lists and debate up to the last minute; a few consult psychics, and some research family trees.

In Tanana where dogs outnumber people almost five to one, puppies usually earn their names faster than they can snatch up salmon scraps. Some dog yards are full of Hollywood stars; others, old cars, criminals and famous athletes, depending on the owner's interests.

In Idaho, Joe picked up Spud, a beautiful, pedigreed, English Pointer, bird dog whose real name, Thadieus Harold the Third, was three inches longer than his tail. Sleek, with a pronounced rib cage covered by a gleaming spotted coat, Spud looked like something out of a Norman Rockwell painting.

According to his registration papers, Spud's family had won every trophy in the bird dog field. Joe was anxious to see him do his stuff. The first morning back home, Joe was up early. He and Spud headed for the open fields by the river. Spud took off like a bullet. Joe waited to see spruce hens fly from the tall grass. No game appeared. Joe whistled and watched the tip of Spud's tail zigzag back towards him. The dog shot right on past at fifty mph with his mouth wide open like a scoop shovel. It didn't take Joe long to realize that this dog was a little different. When he returned home Joe told his wife Sherry, "That dog Spud has a hearing problem! He must have misheard and thinks he's a bug dog, not a bird dog!"

So much for bird hunting. Spud was busy day and night nonstop scooping up bugs in the grass. He rarely touched dog food but still put on weight. Best of all, there was hardly a mosquito in town that summer.

His new Alaskan name became "Skeeter Eater."

John Starr, a local old-timer, waved me over as I walked up River Street against a strong head wind. We both turned our backs to the wind and opened our parka hood ruffs just enough to communicate without shouting. "I have a good dog for you, Mike," John said in his short, direct fashion.

I smiled, nodded and said, "Thanks," and we closed up our wolverine ruffs and leaned back into the frigid blow. Without another word we walked side-by-side the half mile through the village to John's cabin.

I was the cheechako in town, spending every available moment away from my job as RN at the small hospital. I was rebuilding a cabin upriver from town and hoped to put a dog team together. This would be the second dog John had given me in a month. I guessed that I had passed the test, and John liked the way I treated Streisand, his old team leader. John was a respected dog driver in the village. I felt honored to have him support my efforts at building a team.

"This is Cindy," John said as he tried to control the skinny, short-haired dog that was bouncing up and down at the end of the leash, making his cabin seem all that much smaller. I shuffled side to side, trying to avoid being knocked over by this extra friendly pup that looked part Wile E. Coyote and acted purebred Mexican jumping bean. Suddenly, everything went blurry. In a millisecond I had been slimed. As I cleaned the thick film off of my eyeglasses, Cindy finally sat back on her haunches, licking her chops with a big smile. She appeared satisfied with our formal introduction.

"John, do you mind if I call her Lips?" I asked. With a grin, he shook his head slowly.

Lips proved to be a hard-pulling, spirited hound. She did, however, have one minor flaw. Often when I stopped to check the mail or even to blow my nose, Lips would back out of her harness and be off on an adventure. I tried everything except Chinese handcuffs to keep that dog in the towline. Several times I spent all day wandering around the village searching for her. Enraged, my hair on end and neck veins bulging when I finally found her, Lips would run to me with her tail flailing like a fan and her tongue extended. She would leap into my arms. It was impossible to be upset with her for long.

A friend Skip came to visit from Fairbanks. He was standing in the dog yard when he asked how I came up with all the names for the dogs. Lips had just slipped her collar, sprinted over, jumped up, and in a flash had French-kissed Skip. "Her name is Lips," I said as he spit over and over.

"No need to explain. I understand," he added.

"And this pretty Husky over here, his name is Squirt," I said, continuing to introduce the team. Skip said he just as soon not know why I named him Squirt. I advised him to stay clear because Squirt was extra friendly.

During spring races, Dave Webb, the village preacher, asked to borrow Lips for his team. I warned him that at times she didn't stick with the team. Ah, but that was no problem for Dave. We wished him well at the race chute when they took off. Ten minutes later I looked up and coming back down the trail—alone—was Lips, wagging her tail and smiling. I guessed she wasn't in the mood for racing that day.

Later, Dave told us how he had stopped to untangle a pair of swing dogs. When he stood up, Lips was unhooked and heading home. He got disqualified. Her name was lengthened to Houdini Lips.

My leader was Streisand, the first dog given to me by John Starr. She was a big Samoyed-Siberian husky. The first night she was with me I heard a spine-chilling howl. I thought Streisand must be getting eaten by a grizzly bear.

After checking the yard and seeing her with her nose to the sky, I knew what John had been thinking when he named her: She sang like Barbra. I went back to bed, burying my head under every pillow in the house. I reminded myself that it was her "song" which let the world know how happy she really was.

Alex

After escaping from Hungary, Alex fixed TV sets in Harlem for seven years. Seeking quiet and racing to beat the city's summer heat, he loaded his old, Chevy pickup with a canoe, snowshoes and enough food for half a year. As he headed to Alaska, Alex waved to the New York skyline in the early morning June haze as his pickup rolled across the George Washington Bridge.

That summer Alex canoed several rivers of interior Alaska. In September, he found the place of his boyhood dreams. There he set up a wall tent on the Nowitna River, a winding tributary of the Yukon, northwest of Mt. McKinley. He was as far as he could get from Hungary, Harlem and civilization. There were moose, wolves and bears. Alex trapped marten and beaver from a five-mile radius around his camp. Twice a year Alex canoed down the Nowitna to the Yukon, then downriver thirty miles to Ruby, a small Athabascan village.

Years passed. In 1980, Congress designated a two million acre block of land around the Nowitna River as a wildlife refuge, one of sixteen created as part of the Alaska National Interest Lands Conservation Act.

Alex was so isolated it was two years before he even heard about the act. Then the planners, biologists and managers began to show up. The U.S. Fish and Wildlife Department established headquarters in the downriver village of Galena.

On a sunny, summer morning, the refuge officials landed a floatplane on the river in front of Alex's cabin. After introductions they proceeded to read the new rules of the refuge to the forty-year-old trapper. They said he could keep one of the small trapping cabins he had built, but other cabins would have to be taken down or burned. The cabin they were now sitting in was the property of the U.S. government. Alex would be allowed to use it, but he couldn't change anything without written approval. That meant no new windows, no shelves, and only minor repairs.

Alex sat frozen. He gripped his coffee cup tightly, flashing back to when he was a child and the big boys had come to take his father's farm in Hungary. His eyes were focused on the fresh, green uniforms with shiny buttons. Alex was convinced this was all a bad dream. This couldn't be happening, not on the Novi.

Several days later on a sandbar below Alex's camp, a striking, young woman named Barbara introduced herself to Alex as a federal wildlife refuge planner from Anchorage. She said that she would be spending the next couple of weeks in the area. Alex was leery at best and really didn't want to meet any more government people.

She was nice, wanted to talk, and asked Alex many questions about winter alone in the Bush. Over the next two weeks Barbara stopped by in her skiff several times. Summer was fading fast when Barbara stopped by on her final trip to Galena. She asked Alex if it would be okay to visit next January to experience running dogs and winter in the Alaska interior. Alex said sure, as he had told many other summer visitors that he never saw again.

On the 9 p.m. Trapline Chatter (messages announced over KGMP radio as a courtesy to those phoneless in the Bush) from Fairbanks, Alex caught a message to himself. It said, "To Alex on the Nowitna, I'll be out the third Saturday of January; hope that's okay. Barbara." Alex was surprised *and* excited! A guest was a welcomed thought, since this was the loneliest time of year with the severe cold and long nights.

At a retirement party for a co-worker in Anchorage, Barbara was told by the Nowitna Refuge Manager Jim Fisher that she could not visit Alex on the Novi. Fisher went on to explain that it would be conflict of interest for a U.S. Fish and Wildlife planner to spend personal time with the only full-time resident of the refuge. After the party, Fisher appealed to Barbara's supervisor to stop her. He refused.

As refuge manager, Fisher had the power to cite individuals who violated refuge rules or policies. At the time there was no clear rule regarding guests in refuge cabins. Policy was being made on the spot.

The manager's interpretation was that only permit holders and their immediate families could stay in a subsistence cabin. Barbara's visit was considered recreational and the Alaska Lands Act did not permit "private recreational uses" of the cabins within the wildlife refuge. Fisher told Barbara he would write a citation for every day that she stayed in Alex's cabin.

Several days before Barbara was to arrive, a Super Cub rigged with skis landed on the frozen river in front of Alex's cabin. It was the government man, Fisher, in the fancy uniform from Galena. Alex hadn't seen another human for several months. In the past he would always be excited to have visitors, especially in the middle of winter. Now he was being cautious: this man had never brought good news. What could be so important for him to fly out at thirty below zero?

Fisher carried his rule book in hand and stood as if waiting to be invited in. Alex blocked the entrance with arms crossed, a shoulder close to each doorjamb. It was obvious to Fisher he wasn't being invited in no matter whose cabin this was.

Mr. Government scanned the yard with that landlord look and said, "Alex, I forgot to tell you last summer that this is only a work cabin, not a recreation cabin." He hesitated, then added, "So you can't have guests!"

Alex felt like he was going to pass out. Then he felt his chest pounding. He wanted to dive for the man's throat. Mr. Government first apologized and then explained how the rules say that any guests at a work cabin must set up their own tent. "Anyone that violates this rule will be cited, and it will go on your record, Alex." Alex was stunned. A few more rules were read that didn't make sense, and then the unwelcome visitor got back in his Super Cub and flew off.

Barbara continued as planned, but added a wall tent to her list. The refuge manager had agreed that he would not write her a citation as long as she didn't sleep in Alex's cabin.

The last Saturday of January, a Cessna 170 landed on the Nowitna. As the engine shut down and the prop quit spinning, Barbara stepped out onto the ski. Alex was very surprised that she actually made it. After lugging her gear up the riverbank trail to the cabin, they sat down for tea. Comparing notes on the new regulations, Barbara explained how she had gotten the word from the refuge manager in Anchorage. He had read her the rule book in great detail about visiting Alex on the Novi, so she had brought a small tent and a good sleeping bag.

After touring Alex's dog yard, Barbara set up camp on the bluff 150 feet from the cabin, as the rules required.

Even at minus twenty-five degrees, Barbara proved that she could camp out for the first several days. Then a friend flew in to take Alex to town so he could sell his furs. Barbara stayed to take care of the dogs. She moved into the cabin to watch over things for Alex while he was gone.

Three times while Alex was gone, Fisher and a government pilot flew out to the refuge, landed and walked up to Alex's cabin. One time they entered the cabin supposedly to check on the smoking stove.

Each time she heard the small plane coming, Barbara rushed to hide in the bushes to avoid being cited and possibly risking her career. She even stashed a bedroll and food under the brush in case they decided to stay very long.

When Alex returned and learned of the past few days' events, he was furious! He and Barbara decided to move to another cabin that was located off the refuge. They loaded the dogsled and fueled up the snowmachine to break trail. They both felt like criminals, but had no idea what the actual crime was.

Alex did his best to entertain Barbara. He let her run the dogs and showed her how he set his beaver snares. They enjoyed the incredible area around Alex's home as much as possible, considering the frequent visits of Sky King, or as Alex began to call him, "King Fisher." Overhead he circled, with his ticket-book and camera, to record any violations the trapper from Hungary might make while living in the middle of the largest, freest, state in the nation.

Barbara's trip to the wilderness turned out much different than she had expected!. Leaving the bustling city of Anchorage to experience the peaceful isolation of winter turned into a semi-fugitive nightmare.

After his winter guest returned to her job in Anchorage, recent events slowly soaked under Alex's skin. He often had bad dreams and flashbacks of his boyhood days in Hungary when the Communists had come to his family's farm.

In 1987 Alex filed suit against Fisher in the U.S. District Court in Fairbanks. Alex claimed he was denied his constitutional right to associate with whomever he pleased, and that his cabin had been illegally searched. He also claimed the government unnecessarily interfered with his life, causing extreme stress.

For two years the U.S. Justice Department fought the suit. Then U.S. District Judge, Andrew Kleinfeld in Fairbanks issued a judgment saying that Alex and others like him have the right to visitors, as long as the guests don't jeopardize the refuge.

The case of Alex vs. the United States Fish and Wildlife Service was settled out of court. Alex received $40,000 for damages.

Fisher has since been transferred to the agency's main office in Washington, D.C. Hopefully, he is not in charge of the "Romance on the Refuge" Department.

Mother-In-Law

The eight hundred pounds of frozen chicken and horse liver gave the old station wagon good traction on the polished winter streets of Fairbanks.

I was helping Stan get ready for the Iditarod. Hauling a half ton of frozen meat was just another one of my chores.

I didn't worry about my load getting soft. The local thermometer had been stuck at minus forty-five degrees for the past two weeks, and the wagon's heater was such a poor one, it barely kept my toes alive. Just to be safe, I covered the mound of fifty-pound blocks with two, old, green, Army blankets.

The last day in town included a trip to Nenana, fifty miles west on the Parks Highway. The road was along a ridge overlooking the Tanana River.

I was going to Nenana Fuel Company. Whenever I wanted to get paid, which was about every six months, I would have to resign my position as the Tanana fuel distributor. My boss would get the hint and pay up.

As the overloaded wagon climbed the long hill out of Ester, the fog thinned. Suddenly, there was blue sky, and visibility went from one hundred feet to a hundred miles. It reminded me of coming up out of the New York subway into the bright lights of Times Square.

With the sun's warmth through the windshield, I even took my beaver mitts off for awhile.

The past three days in town had gone without a catch. The old wagon started every time, a rarity at these temperatures. I credited the extra heavy load with keeping me on the road.

In Nenana I sat and waited, growing anxious as the sun began to dip below the horizon. I preferred to drive in daylight if possible. The thought of digging under all that frozen meat for a spare tire or tool in the dark made me cringe.

At last, back in business with a pocket of cash, I bought new harnesses, sled parts and a half ton of pure protein. I still had enough dollars for Stan to run the Iditarod. I left Nenana and headed back to Fairbanks.

Descending the last hill into town, the ice fog wrapped around the loaded wagon like a quilt. I let up on the gas and tried to focus through the thick, cotton candy-like wall that headlights only seemed to make worse.

One more stop on the list—Jimmy Anderson's, next to the airport. The turn appeared suddenly. I tried for it and started sliding sideways. At first the heavy car handled well, weaving side to side. Then I knew the ditch was mine.

Tightly gripping the steering wheel, I locked my arms straight and prayed that all that chicken wouldn't come forward. The mention of fifty-pound blocks of frozen liver and chicken was not something I wanted in my obituary.

When all motion and noise ceased, I opened my eyes. The car was propped at a forty-five degree angle, front bumper in the powdery, dry snow, rear end high in the air.

"Damn! We almost made it!" I thought as I wrestled one fifty-pound block back over the seat and covered it with the blankets. When I realized that the big, new dent in the dash had just been caused by a chunk of flying frozen liver, I was grateful the others had stayed put.

It was colder out now, maybe minus fifty. I could feel it when I climbed up the bank. My nose hair felt like it had been fiberglassed. Not dressed for hiking, I ran toward town, taking short breaths so as not to freeze my lungs.

The second house with lights on had a 4x4 pickup in the drive with big knobby tires like the ones you see on the piston-head magazines in the supermarket.

I knocked hard.

A huge man answered in his T-shirt and pants. From what I could see through my frosted eyelashes, I would bet that Thanksgiving was his favorite day of the year by the way his belt disappeared in the front.

I said, "Please, sir, I'm nose down in the ditch. I'll pay ya to give me a yank."

I pointed back to the corner with a cold, desperate look. He hesitated. I thought maybe I needed to offer one hundred pounds of ground-up liver. I kept the pitiful look.

After what seemed like eternity, in a slow, Southern drawl he said, "Well, okay Sonny, I'll try it." I ran back to the car and kicked the snow so I could crawl under and attach the tow strap.

My new friend pulled up in his fancy monster pickup. He climbed out waving a flashlight that you could land a jumbo jet with.

"Sonny, you sure are stuck here." He shined the light at the rear bumper which was three feet in the air, then walked slowly around with the spotlight. The squeaking of his bunny boots stopped.

"Sonny, what's that dripping off your front bumper down there?" I figured it was antifreeze and poked my head around to look. There were bright red spots in the snow, with more dripping along the side all the way up to the back door. I quickly surmised that the rear heater vent under the pile of race food was working much better than the one up front.

He stood rigid. The light didn't move an inch until I said, "Oh, damn, my mother-in-law is in the back. She must be thawing out."

The light flashed on the thawing mound in the back, still covered with Army blankets.

I tried to ease the tension. "Yep, I haul her around for better traction."

The jumbo landing light went out, and then I heard the quick CRUNCH CRUNCH of fleeing, king-sized bunny boots. A truck door slammed. The pickup raced away backwards.

I stood there in the dark and thought, "Maybe I should have passed that line by."

If I had known there were two recent, unsolved murders just up the road, I'd have insisted he take the liver from the start.

Dr. Jim

Dr. Jim was one of our village doctors at the small, Indian hospital in Tanana. He and his wife Felicia, a petite Puerto Rican, had moved from California with their small daughters, June and Eileen. It soon became obvious that very little could slow them down. As a family, they hitchhiked boat rides from the Natives on the Yukon, Kobuk or Koyukuk Rivers. When necessary, they each carried one of the girls.

One spring, Dr. Jim, Felicia and the girls made it to Barrow for whaling season. They helped the locals pull the first whale onto the ice and joined in the celebration. That summer they floated down nearly every river in Alaska and, by the end of the next winter, had put together a dog team.

The days were getting longer. There was a lot of movement on the river ice. Everyone was visiting and traveling, either by snowmachine or dog team. Jim and Felicia loaded up their dog sled and headed forty miles north to the Tozitna to visit Stan and Helen Zuray. They had wanted to make the trip all winter and finally, due to unlimited sunshine, couldn't wait any longer. The wind was blowing hard on the flats along the way. Felicia was bundled up in the sled with both girls. All three were wrapped in sleeping bags.

Stan and Helen's place is protected by tall spruce trees. So, when the family arrived, the wind had ceased and it was calm and warm as any spring day in the Interior.

Stan and Helen put on a big feed. They didn't get much company way out there. They wanted to catch up on all the news. They knew the bigger the meal, the more captive they could keep the village people, which meant more local gossip.

June interrupted the conversation by pulling on Jim's shirt. She said she had to pee. Jim grabbed her and asked Stanley which way to the outhouse.

Stanley had dug a brand new outhouse the past fall and had built a small teepee over it out of brush and spruce bows. He hadn't had time to mill any lumber for a deluxe model yet.

Jim carried June to the outhouse and propped her on the crossbar. The hole was a bit bigger than usual. Stanley had plans to make a Styrofoam circular seat. But for now June was balanced on a small cross beam as Jim searched for toilet paper. After picking up two empty coffee cans, he reached way over to a small box that he hoped held some old magazines or something to use in place of toilet paper.

When Dr. Jim later told the story, he said he didn't have any memory of letting go. But when he turned around, June was gone. He hated to look. Jim stuck his head over the large square hole and saw his youngest daughter six feet below with a look like "Dad, why?" As if that weren't bad enough, Felicia had just come out to enjoy the sunshine and from the distance through the thin spruce branches she could see Jim kneeling in the outhouse, but no June!

Felicia let go with a hysterical, "Jim, where's my daughter? Where's June?" She had to know; why else would Jim be kneeling in the outhouse, talking down into the hole and shaking his head?

44 ❖ **Return to the River**

Cosmic Mortgage

Ricky was a refreshing addition to the village. He moved to Tanana to work as manager of the power and phone company. His heritage was half Puerto Rican, half Mexican. Ricky's long, gangly body was topped with thick, black hair.

The first time we met was on the riverbank one June evening. Ricky stood behind a large, gray cat that sat staring at the river. After a brief introduction, Ricky pointed to his cat Smokey and said, "We just moved from the Kenai River and my poor cat is all confused because this river is going the opposite direction."

We became friends and visited each other often. Ricky told many stories about growing up in East L.A. and about his two terms as a tank driver in Viet Nam. My favorite tale was how his tank had been blown up and the last thing he remembered was flying through the air. Then everything went black. A long line of bright, white stars appeared through the surrounding darkness. His first thought was that this must be the Milky Way and he was on his way to heaven. Slowly, his sense of feeling returned. Ricky spit out a mouth full of dirt and painfully tried to move his right leg. A loud, scared voice yelled, "That bag is moving! I swear!" quickly followed by ZZZZZZZZIPPP. The bright sunlight blinded Ricky as his buddies peeled him from the crusty body bag. So much for the trip to heaven.

Ricky told that story and many more like it as if they were everyday occurrences.

Many of the villagers appreciated his "at ease" approach and "take care of business anytime" attitude. Finding your place in a small village is not easy and often takes years. Ricky held the record in my book for being accepted and respected.

It was nice to have someone we didn't worry about. Most often, newcomers to the village would go to extremes within a year, becoming alcoholics or religious fanatics. Ricky was solid. We never worried for a second.

With the long June days, I would often be up late working on fishwheel baskets or running dogs on the beach. Rattling and clanging, Ricky's old utility truck would come bouncing up my narrow, rutted drive.

I welcomed his late visits which included enthusiastic plans ranging from farming the tundra to guiding tourists on river trips. He would grab my guitar and sit in the old wicker chair, picking any tune mentioned.

"Mike," he beamed one evening, "I was visiting today with that new store manager. He's really an interesting guy. He knows world history inside out. The Constitution and how this country came together is his main interest."

He told me about his church and its beliefs: "Mike, you know what? If you go by the rules and work your way up, after you die you get your own planet."

"My own planet?" I thought to myself. Surely he was only kidding. I waited.

Ricky expounded on the benefits of working hard, having lots of children and getting your own planet. Still I waited for the punch line, hoping this was an East L.A. joke, but he kept right on talking. Finally, he paused and waited for my response.

I said in as serious a tone as I could muster, "Ricky, don't you think maybe you should get your own house or even a car before you worry about getting your own planet?"

He didn't appreciate my response.

Ricky had made it a year in the village. I couldn't believe he was going to short out now. I tried to humor him.

Then I thought, "My God, he expected me to sign up for my own planet as well." I told Ricky that if I were him, I would do a little more homework before I signed anything. It sounded more like the Church of the Great Real Estate Deal to me.

Later that summer, several of us were trying to buy a small piece of land above the village from the Episcopal

Church. Ricky was trying to scrape up enough money for a five-acre piece.

One morning, discouraged, Ricky stopped in to share his money woes. Sean, a good friend from the old neighborhood, was visiting and had caught up on village happenings, including Ricky's plan to get his own planet. Sean listened, then looked up from breakfast and lifted his eyebrows.

"Rick, it sounds to me like you have the planet in the bag. Do you think you could get a Cosmic Mortgage on your planet to pay off your five acres on the hill?"

Although Sean's comments failed to humor him, Ricky *did* seem to be contemplating the possibility.

Bigger Boom

I picked up the phone. It was the village mayor. In an anxious voice he almost begged, "Will you pick up a load of dynamite this afternoon?" I asked for the details. He informed me the city of Tanana was selling gravel from a pit a half mile upriver, and more blasting needed to be done.

Winter was moving in fast and, after a long weekend, the construction projects were well behind schedule. The ground had frozen, and the big backhoes were wearing out trying to break the surface.

"I'll send an expert with you," he offered.

"Great, because I wouldn't know a box of TNT from Tootsie Rolls," I replied.

I fueled up the plane, and the expert who arrived was none other than our local preacher, Dave Webb.

Dave told a few stories as we readied for take off. He made it sound as if he had blown up everything in Oklahoma at least once.

The trip to town was bumpy. Thick clouds set up an obstacle course.

After landing at the nearly deserted Metro Air Field, a rough-looking character whose face and hands looked like he had played a major role in more than one too many explosions, backed his pickup truck to my Cherokee side door.

I wasn't convinced this was legal. The way he furiously loaded the cases, it looked like we had just heisted Fort Knox.

During the long flight I looked over my shoulder several times, wishing I could trade this load for the pigs and chickens I had hauled and dreaded so much the previous spring. Then I noticed Dave was reading the instructions on the box of caps. My anxiety level instantly peaked, along with my imagination. One more look and some basic math told me I was in close company with seven hundred sticks of dynamite. That seemed like more than enough to help me become the first man on the moon without a spaceship if the TNT decided to get excited. I didn't look back again for the remainder of that flight and finally landed extra carefully.

While we had been making the flight to Fairbanks, an ancient, military track rig had drilled blast holes in the gravel pit. Under Preacher Dave's supervision, the bundles of sticks were stuffed into fifteen holes, a cord strung between each. Then loads of dirt were dumped over each hole. The mounds looked like a giant gopher town.

Many of the villagers were lined up along the road. The detonator cord ran behind the loader. A warning was yelled to get back. Very few of the spectators had ever seen dynamite used. We all peeked from behind vehicles. Then the cord was sparked.

A concussion wave pushed at my chest. Kids cried as they covered their ears. Mudballs, some the size of prize-winning watermelons, went skyward from fifteen cannon holes. No one moved until the airborne confetti settled.

The ridge looked the same, except the dirt mounds were gone. The frozen ground had worked like large gun barrels. "The holes aren't deep enough and we need more dirt on top," our resident expert concluded.

It became apparent from the amazed look on Dave's face that he hadn't had much experience with blasting ice back in Oklahoma.

"That was good, but we want a bigger boom," the honorable mayor announced. Several of his cronies nodded slowly as if they weren't quite sure.

Elizabeth and Al, two God-fearing neighbors whose home sits just across from the pit, hadn't been warned. They were sitting down to dinner when the first boom hit. They began praying full speed; the time to repent had arrived. Heavy pounding on the metal roof and mud balls showering the yard encouraged the whole family into the garage.

The drying laundry still hung on the lines out back, only now with small chunks of thawing tundra suspended in Pop's clean shorts. "So this is the end of the world," Al thought as he ducked back into the garage.

The second boom was bigger. It broke up the frozen ground. Most of this gravel was used for the final stage of the new HUD housing program. Each of the twenty-five new homes built that summer needed its own outhouse built to a standard written by some man in a suit and tie somewhere in the Lower 48.

Next to each new home an elevated trail led to a circle of gravel piled six feet high. Since the tundra doesn't perk particularly well, these one-seater outhouses had to sit that high, looking more like Russian monuments.

The job was almost finished. After final inspection, big federal checks would be disbursed. There wasn't time to break up the beachball-size gravel. So that fall, twenty-five new outhouses each sat high, balancing precariously on what looked like a stack of meatballs.

The local Indians aren't only a bit superstitious, but they're also smart. The twenty thousand dollar outhouses sat new all winter.

Zat's Impossible

"If you don't show me za trail on zis map now, tomorrow I'll take my compass and snowshoe north to find Russ and Ann Vood's homestead."

"Blacky," I said loudly, "it's minus fifty degrees, and the wind is blowing like hell on the ridge, which means there's no snow on the flats. Sit tight, at least until the wind lets up, so you can make it alive for Christmas dinner!"

I had been tying a dog sled together in the front room. Blacky was lying on the floor in the kitchen telling Louie, Lynda and Claire where he was going to snowshoe that December in interior Alaska.

We were all concerned. Poor judgment in the winter was often fatal in the Alaska bush.

At breakfast Blacky was packed and still angry with me for not giving him the directions to Russ's until I said, "You take the dogs and new sled. I'll drive the sno-go."

He lit up and said in his thick German, "Vill you go too?"

"Yep, Blacky, I must be even dumber than you are," I volunteered. "We'll have lots of fun, Blacky, especially in the overflow."

"Vhat's zat?"

"That's where the streams freeze solid and the water runs on top," I added with a smile.

"Oh, zat's impossible," he laughed. "You like to tell stories, and last night you said zere would be no snow on za flats. Well, zere's four feet right here. You must like za way I fix your cuckoo clock and split your wood."

"That's for sure, Blacky, but more than that, I don't want to have to go looking for you."

We hitched eight, frisky hounds to my new, oak sled. Blacky jumped on the runners as I banged the ice hook free with the butt end of an ax. I hollered, "I'll catch up. Ride the brake."

From the rear, Blacky looked like a slalom water skier, as snow shot up in a "V" from the sled brake. Loud, mispronounced swear words rang out in the frigid air.

While I finished my tea, Lynda and Louie called their bets on our return time. They agreed we'd be back in four hours. "This guy is a real case. He needs a good camp-out at this temperature to cure him," I said as I finished packing my survival gear.

After seven miles, I could see Blacky pushing the loaded sled up the steep trail of Twelve-Mile Hill. I waited and raced up when he and the dogs crested the hill. Two long icicles hung from Blacky's mustache. His beard was as white as the trim on a wedding cake.

"Whatever you do, don't break a sweat. Slow down if you need," I yelled in the wind. "It'll probably be blowing harder on that next ridge."

We continued along the series of small hills that form the south ridge of the Tozitna Valley. Then we dropped down the long, sidehill trail into Ptarmigan Valley. Blacky was snugging up his parka and hood as the dogs pranced down the hard-packed, windblown snow. The new P-Tex sled runners glided so fast that the wheel dogs' main concern was avoiding getting run over by the sled. Blacky switched feet on the brake. Nearing the bottom of the draw, the light, powdery snow on the trail began to get deeper. I stopped and waited for Blacky, who glided up with only his eyes visible through a mask of frost.

"Blacky, you have to keep up speed after this next dip to cross the creek. It's probably full of overflow. I'll race through to set a trail."

"Overflow!" he grumbled. "Zat's impossible!" A muffled chuckle followed. He still thought I was pushing a joke.

I gave the old sno-go full throttle and stood with one knee on the seat to see over the hazed windshield. I felt the machine bog down as I dropped into the creek bed. Rocking the machine from side to side, I spun the track in the thick slush, finally waddling the thirty feet across to firm ground.

I waved back to Blacky. He yelled, "Mush!" The dogs sprinted and leaped to avoid the cold water. The sled jerked. Blacky hung on tight, leaning over the curved handlebar as his canvas mukluks dragged in the slush.

When they pulled up next to me, the dogs were excited to be on dry snow. They kicked and bit the snow from their foot pads.

Blacky puffed thick bursts of steam as he stood staring back at the gray trail of saturated snow he had just splashed through.

Shaking his head, he said once again, but with a bit less conviction, "Zat's impossible."

Peace

The cabins in the distance were a welcome sight. After two weeks canoeing the Peace River, my friend Janice and I were anxious to meet the local folks.

We had put in at Fort Vermilion in northern Alberta, planning to canoe the Peace and Smith rivers to Great Slave Lake by freeze-up that fall.

The Peace River is wide and slow except for one set of three-mile-long rapids. Anticipating the Vermilion shoots (Native term for rapids) added to the excitement of being in the wilderness for the first week. At the fort, we had received conflicting stories on the shoots. While we loaded our canoe, two teenage Cree boys stood watching.

When I asked them about the shoots, the spokesman shrugged his shoulders and said very matter-of-factly, "No big deal," as if he might canoe them every day before lunch. A friendly old-timer in the Hudson Bay Store, however, told us, "There's a good trail around the shoots," as if there was no question that we would portage.

Several miles upriver from the rapids we could hear a faint rumble. Soon the speed of the river increased and that sound grew into a deafening roar. Then shrouded in a thick mist ahead, we could see the froth and foam of the white water.

Jan looked back from her kneeling position in the bow of the canoe. We traded last-minute questioning looks, then both slowly shook our heads in definite agreement.

With paddles dug deep, we strained for shore. The loaded canoe fought us as if it wanted to challenge these rapids. A breeze lifted the mist for only seconds, allowing us to see clearly the deep swells only yards ahead. It was obvious we wouldn't have a chance if sucked into that torrent. With one final surge of adrenaline, we nosed the bow into an overhang of alders. Jan gripped the thickest branch and pulled it to her chest while the canoe swung, putting me only a few feet from the first dip of what looked more like waterfalls. From there we sat catching our breaths.

After gladly portaging the three-mile trail, we reloaded and glided back into the river. Looking back upriver at what turned out to be a close relative to Niagara Falls, we both sighed with relief.

The second week into our trip the river widened and seemed to almost come to a halt. A steady, upriver wind made us work for any progress. One day we sat it out on the bank, watching driftwood get blown back upstream. I looked at the map every few hours and swore I would never travel a slow river again. Jan, rarely big on conversation, sat sewing leather knee patches on her jeans.

The past several days, I had the feeling Jan was enjoying this wilderness adventure a lot more than I. While I worried about making good mileage and complained that we hadn't met any of the local Cree Indians, Jan seemed to take it all in stride, never getting excited unless we were about to go over a waterfall.

Then I said, "I don't see what's so wild about the wilderness: The animals all run away from us and all this quiet could make ya crazy. I don't know about you, but I could use a little excitement." Jan smiled, as she often did when I exaggerated a scene.

Soon afterward, cabins, which sat in the outside curve of the oxbow, came into view. We nosed the canoe onto the sandy beach and tied the canoe to a small cottonwood. A wide rutted trail cut diagonally across the forty-foot-high bank, up to a grassy meadow.

We unloaded the canoe and packed the tent and sleeping bags to a level spot at the base of the trail. Before we set up the tent, I suggested we go meet the locals. Jan and I hiked up to the grassy flat where the rustic cabins stood.

Not knowing what or who to expect, I tried to slow down. My excitement was obvious. I lightly knocked on the narrow, gray-planked door. A middle-aged Indian opened it quickly, startling us, then saying, "Come in, come in. You are the Americans." I suddenly felt like a guest of honor. How had he known?

He completed my thought. "Word travels fast on the river."

His name was Phillip and his pretty Cree wife was Angelina. Extra chairs were moved to the table that was set with tea and cookies. Two small children stared at us.

Phillip started, "We don't see many travelers on the river anymore. In the sixties we had lots of visitors from all over. We like to meet new people." We visited over tea as the sun set, putting a light. golden hue over the river.

Almost dark, I suggested we had better go set up camp. We emptied our tea cups. Phillip invited us back for cake later, because today was Angelina's thirtieth birthday.

While we set up camp, Jan and I talked about how friendly these people were and how great it was to travel the rivers of the North and have such hospitality along the way.

Camp set, we returned to our new friends' cabin. A fancy cake and two small gifts were centered on the table. Phillip lit the candles, and we all sang "Happy Birthday" to Angelina. She was blushing, so she could barely get enough pucker to blow the candles out.

With my instamatic camera I took pictures of the two kids smearing icing ear-to-ear and of Phillip wearing a tiny, cone hat.

My definition of heaven wasn't far from this.

A loud knock on the door stopped the action. Angelina yelled, "Come in!" A lanky, rugged-looking, long-haired Indian stooped through the doorway with a short, heavy friend in tow.

"We have come all the way from Fort Chip to celebrate my sister's birthday," were the tall one's first words as he set a gallon jug of wine on the table next to the cake.

Introductions were quick and of little interest to the newcomers, as evidenced by their limp handshakes and vague eye contact. Angelina's brother was named Pierre; his friend was Clifford.

Jan and I moved to the couch, making room at the table. Phillip slid his chair over to join us. Much of the talk at the table was in their native Cree tongue. The wine flowed from small cups, and several toasts were led by Pierre to the greatest sister in the world.

When addressed from the table in Cree, Phillip gave curt, one word answers, then continued his stories for us. He was making every effort to be a good host, but I could see he was getting irritated by the loud talk behind him.

Both children had fallen asleep; the boy in Phillip's lap, the girl next to Jan on the couch. Phillip carried his son through a dull green curtain into the back room and then returned for his daughter.

It was getting late. Pierre and Cliff were singing short songs in Cree, laughing after each verse. I wished I knew what they were saying because Phillip's face seemed to get more irate after each song.

Then he went into the back room. It was quiet for a few seconds while the last of the wine was guzzled in a final toast. That's when I caught the sound of shells being chambered into a rifle from behind the curtain.

I nudged Jan and whispered, "We have to go!" She didn't get my urgency. I excused us as the bleary-eyed threesome turned and nodded.

I tried to explain to Jan as our eyes adjusted to the trail, "I swear I heard a gun being loaded!" Jan looked closely to see if I was joking or just trying to get her to hurry.

Then came Blam! Blam! followed by blood-curdling screams from the cabin only a hundred feet behind us. We ran full speed down to the tent. I wished the canoe were loaded so we could shove off even though it would have been risky. The river was high and loaded with drift logs, but right then, all I wanted was to get far away from this place.

Another round of shots broke the Northern peace, accompanied by a bone-chilling scream. I grabbed my old British Enfield rifle and shells from inside the tent, loading seven into the clip. Jan was almost hysterical. I tried to sound calm as we quickly stuffed the sleeping bags to look as if we were in them. Then we carried the extra blankets up the steep bank and hid in a thick clump of alders, fifty feet from the tent.

We whispered now, trying to figure out what had happened. It was obvious someone was dead, and we were the only people within miles who could be witnesses. I was certain that they would soon be looking for us. "What will we do now?" Jan whispered, as we sat crouched on the steep hillside with the heavy, old war gun resting on my knees.

"When they come looking for us, I will wait until they reach in and discover the sleeping bags are empty, then I will have to blast 'em!" I tried to sound as much like John Wayne as possible. Jan put her head down as if to pray, which is what I'd been doing all along.

The voices speaking Cree were heading our way. I took steady, deep breaths as they got closer. I put the rifle butt to my shoulder and made sure the safety was off. Hours seemed to pass. No visitors came into view. I heard the word *mooniow,* which means *white man.* This added to my anxiety. I snugged the gun tighter to my shoulder.

Thirty feet from the tent Pierre and Clifford took a turn off the trail into the brush towards the water. An outboard motor fired up, and they shoved off downriver into the dark. Whew! I inhaled a long, deep breath.

After relaxing several seconds, it struck me that if anyone was to be dead I would have preferred it to be the two who had just left in good shape. My heart sank; if it wasn't them, then it had to be our new friends.

We tried to sleep huddled on the hillside. Daybreak finally came after several long hours. Gathering enough nerve to return to the cabin, Jan and I walked slowly up the trail. We couldn't make any sense of what we had heard late that night. I prepared myself for the worst, as we reached the top of the bank.

The sun had just crested the eastern horizon. I turned, hoping there really wasn't a cabin and this had all been a bad dream.

But there was Phillip and Angelina waving from the front stoop of their cabin. They looked a bit hung over as they sipped from steaming coffee cups. I tried to nonchalantly look them over, but could not find any bullet wounds or the slightest signs of blood. Phillip handed me a cup of black coffee. I took a sip and causally said, "Things got a little noisy last night at the birthday party," leaving it wide open. They both looked at me as if I'd really said something insulting. I looked over at Jan who seemed as confused as I was. We finished our coffee and bid farewell.

Loading the canoe didn't take long. I must admit that when we shoved off, that big, slow river never looked so good.

Three weeks later in the Northwest Territory we met an old trapper who knew everyone on the river. I got up my nerve to tell him about the birthday party. Old Ira said, "You must have been at Phillip's and Angelina's," as if they were next door neighbors.

Jan and I both nodded. Ira went on, "When things get a little dull Angelina stirs it up until Phillip gets a gun and starts shooting; then she's happy. Did you notice all those little magazine pictures tacked to the wall?"

We both nodded. "Yep," he continued, "they cover the bullet holes." He smiled. "Quite a couple. I'd say a match made in heaven."

Mr. Gravity

Meeting small airplanes that land at village airports is often high on the list of entertainment for the local folk. I've noticed the smaller the town, the bigger the crowd when the plane touches down.

One sunny afternoon in the middle of August, a flashy Central Air Twin Navajo landed in Tanana. One of the first passengers to step out was a tall, curly-haired, handsome character who looked a lot like Eddie Haskell from the '60s TV show "Leave It to Beaver." My best guess was that Mr. Jackman, the principal, had finally found a new coach for the basketball team. The village was in desperate need.

Now I was beginning to feel like a local, able to guess a new arrival's business as soon as he got off the plane. I was sure that Eddie Haskell was our new coach.

He put his bags down on the grass at the edge of the gravel airstrip, then proceeded to stretch and take a couple of short jumps into the air. Well, that confirmed it: I was ready to put all my money down that this was our new coach. And from the looks of his enthusiasm, he would get these Indian kids into the playoffs.

He left his bags and strolled off down the side of the runway. Eddie looked around slowly, side to side. I could only think that this must be a city guy overwhelmed with all this space. He took running starts and then jumped up like he was doing a stuff. I thought he must have been locked up for a few days in the planes getting here. He strolled and jumped his way down the air strip, then disappeared off the end of the runway. He reminded me of when I had first gotten to the village and was in awe of all the room, but he had me beat. He was definitely more enthused than I ever thought of being.

It didn't take long. Word got out that our new man in town wasn't the coach. In fact, one of the old timers ran into him on a trail behind town and asked what he was doing in Tanana, jumping around the outside perimeter of the village. He said he was testing gravity. He said he was heading to Siberia, testing gravity all along the way.

The Athabascan Indians see all kinds of colorful folks floating down the river. Since before the gold rush there has been a flow of oftentimes half-baked Yahoos. Mr. Gravity was a little bit different, but not that far off cue from some of the drifters that had come through. He did spend time down at the Northern Commercial store, entertaining the kids. His theory was this: to really get acquainted with someone you have to be in mid-air; then you have an instant connection. Eddie was convinced that people shouldn't be grounded like we are.

Eddie grabbed the young kids right off the porch of the N.C. store, hooked them under their elbows and leaped into the air—his way of making a good, solid friendship. The kids went along with it.

The nurses put on a dance one Friday night. There was always a shortage of men, so Mr. Gravity must have gotten a written invitation.

After the party was over, Dan Johnson, the night-shift maintenance man, went in to check the dance hall in the basement of the nurses' quarters. He found this stranger sleeping on the couch. Dan kept poking him. Finally Mr. Gravity sat up and, wide-eyed, grabbed Dan under the arms and proceeded to jump across the dance floor with him. Dan had been out of town and didn't know about this new guest in the village. He thought that Eddie was dreaming about the party. Dan went along for a few steps, then decided he had had enough and butted Mr. Gravity hard in the chest. It slowed him down, and finally Dan was let go. Dan didn't wait around for any explanations. He ran to the nurses' station, which was open twenty-four hours, to get help in dealing with the dancing maniac downstairs.

The way it goes in the village, when you have finally had enough of these new characters, you pass the hat. That is what we did; we passed the hat and got Mr. Gravity a ticket downriver to Ruby. We also wished him luck in Siberia.

Six months later a friend from Nome stopped in Tanana. He asked if we had met a guy travelling through here who jumped into the air every couple hundred feet,

"Oh yes, of course, Mr. Gravity." Who else?

Sprouts

The offer sounded a bit more exciting than wrapping up in a chiffon robe each day to sell incense and carnations at the Seattle air terminal.

Tim and Loretta Rayburg had been selected to represent the Hare Krishna religion in Alaska. They were to locate the geographical center—"God's eye"—of the state, build a cabin and live off the land for a year. Focusing mostly on the cosmic energies of the aurora borealis, they were to experience the extreme light and dark seasons, as well as endure the severe cold of interior Alaska. All this was to be accomplished with as few material goods as possible and only one other companion, their Labrador pup, Mantra.

They were chosen because of their past experiences in the wilderness. They had guided canoe trips on the Snake and Missouri rivers in Idaho and Montana during college summer vacations. One last stop at the Bagwan Get One Free health food store in north Seattle to pick up a year's supply of alfalfa seeds, mung beans, lentils, rice, granola, and they were ready to travel. Their sloped-back green,

Volvo station wagon was loaded to the roof. Tim was at the wheel, Mantra in the middle, and Loretta took charge of maps and copiloting as they pulled onto I-5 heading north.

After two days of almost nonstop driving through British Columbia, they rolled into Dawson Creek, the beginning of the dusty Alcan Highway. During an afternoon break at the small community park, Tim ran through his daily yoga routine, bending and flexing. The local farm folk who drove by twisted their necks to get a prolonged view of this rubberized visitor.

A mile north of Dawson, the pavement abruptly stopped. The tightly packed Volvo zinged along the washboard road, leaving a whirling dust cloud behind. To oncoming travelers it looked more like a high-strung turtle weaving through the thick spruce forest of northern British Columbia.

Part of the original deal was that Tim and Loretta could both grow back their hair, trade in their pink, shower curtain-type robes for an Eddie Bauer wardrobe, and not have to smear the Krishna chalk line from nose tip to hairline each morning.

These were two excited, incognito Hare Krishnas heading north. Three dusty days on the bumpy Alcan and they were checking in at the U.S. Border Customs Station. Next stop was Fairbanks, Alaska. Three hundred miles of paved highway carried their now dirt-brown buggy into town.

Nothing could have prepared Tim and Loretta for the boom town that Fairbanks was in 1976: traffic jams,

K-Mart, hookers wearing leopard-skin tights, Winnebagos, and hundred dollar bills trading hands over most counters. This Arctic Circle craziness encouraged them to get their canoe loaded and out onto the Tanana River.

The winding Tanana River slowly carried them west. Often, Tim was convinced they were just going in circles because the sun never set. He didn't realize that in June the sun only dips to the horizon then climbs high again. They set up camp on the muddy banks, fighting off clouds of mosquitoes.

Nenana was the first village to come into sight after paddling two days. Last minute supplies were available at Coghill's small grocery. With the addition of a case of mosquito spray and a fifty-pound sack of dog food, the shiny aluminum canoe sat low. It was time to shove off and head for the Yukon River, 150 miles northwest.

On the fifth day out, they hit Squaw Crossing, a mile-wide shallow stretch with one narrow channel and an endless maze of sandbars. Mantra jumped from the canoe. Running ahead in the shallows, he seemed to sense the current and helped Tim navigate the heavy canoe. Only seriously grounding twice, they glided out of the Tanana onto the Yukon River.

This large river moved faster. Loretta sat lower as she felt the canoe accelerate. The water was clearer. The banks were lined with big rocks and gravel beaches.

"That must be Tanana!" Tim said as he pointed excitedly to the north side of the river. They paddled across the Yukon, then glided the loaded canoe twenty feet from shore.

There were Indians on the bank; a haze of blue smoke hung over the river's edge. Many small sheds along the river had old, green, canvas tarps draped over the doors. Thin plumes of fragrant smoke leaked through the cracks. Tim could see in one of the open doors. There were strips of bright red salmon hanging. From the distance, the strips looked like long strands of red licorice candy.

As they got closer to the village center, the beach came alive with kids playing. Large, scruffy dogs stood up. Chained to old, rusty, gang line cables, they tilted their heads back and howled in unison. Many had caves dug back under the ledge, but all were now at the end of their chains, welcoming the new visitors.

The adults didn't seem very excited to see strangers. Tim tried to control his waving. The kids stared out at the colorful canoeist while some of the old people waved slowly.

A large Northern Commercial sign hung on a building just up from the barge unloading ramp. Tim steered the canoe around a long river boat and into a slip. Loretta climbed out and tied the bow line to a huge, half-buried, rusty metal wheel.

An inverted wooden boat in front of the NC store was a bench for a group of old-timers—short, stocky, handsome, tan Indians. They all smiled as Tim crested the bank.

"Where you come from?" asked the spokesman.

"Seattle," Tim answered politely.

"That's a long way in a canoe." They all had a good chuckle. It helped Tim relax.

The store had everything but for outrageous prices. Milk at eight dollars a gallon, eggs at five dollars—Tim couldn't think of much they needed.

Strolling the narrow dirt roads of the small village, they were amazed at all the dogs tied up, the number of small children, and how close the cabins were to each other. A few old vehicles rumbled and rattled along, making independent dust clouds.

Back on the bank above their canoe, the old-timers still sat on their perch, now looking upriver toward the confluence of the Tanana and the Yukon.

"Barge coming today, just above Squaw Crossing now. Water real low this year," the spokesman announced.

Tim listened. He couldn't hear a barge. The old-timers must have traditional ways to tell, he thought. That's when old Lee Edwin pointed up and said, "Airplane pilot tell us lots." Tim tried to control his grin, then nodded slowly.

Tim and Loretta shook hands with all six gentlemen on the boat. "We plan to stay on the Tozitna River this winter," Tim added.

Old Lee perked up. "It's cold and windy out there." He pointed behind the village. "Ravens live there!"

Lee was small, almost shriveled up. His eyes were big with a gleam. His hands moved smoothly as he talked in broken English. He seemed to enjoy keeping the others laughing. His hair was white and to guess his age would be tough, but Tim would bet close to one hundred. After sitting with them twenty minutes, however, Tim changed his guess. Because of the way Lee entertained and the energy that he radiated, Tim thought he was probably closer to forty.

Tim and Loretta said good-bye and shook hands again.

Lee used his cane to stand up, then said, "Good luck, Gunna," to Tim.

It was quite a welcome. At first having felt like intruders, the little man had now made them feel more at home than they could ever remember.

The Tozitna runs into the Yukon ten miles downriver from Tanana. It didn't take long to get there, with the rapid current of the mighty river. Navigating up the narrow Tozitna was work. Tim ended up poling and lining most of the forty-five miles to the spot they picked to winter, a plateau fifty feet above the narrow river. The view was spectacular—the Ray Mountains to the north, the flats stretching to the Caribou Hills to the south.

Most of August was spent carrying large, flat river rocks onto the plateau to build a tiny rock shelter. The fireplace worked for heat and cooking. Overhead, narrow black spruce poles covered by a large tarp kept the crude hut dry. Two small visqueen windows and a pole door with canvas hinges tucked them in for the winter. Using a bow saw, they collected dry wood from the log jams in the river's curves. Their Bauer sleeping bags on top of air mattresses were as comfortable as a Sealy Posturepedic.

At night they often left the door open so they could see the spectacular aurora late into September.

Days were growing shorter at an incredible rate; now only mid-October, it was a rush to get the day's chores completed. The ice on the tiny slough was thickening so fast it seemed each morning was consumed with retrieving a pail of water. The afternoons were spent stocking the daily wood supply.

The peaceful time was at night. Tucked in their sleeping bags, they could stare out at the shimmering aurora. The hypnotic magic of the lights, along with Tim and Loretta's complete physical exhaustion, made sleep a welcomed friend.

The small, stone cabin was far from air-tight. When the wind blew, which it most often did on the Tozitna, the newcomers would wake in the early hours with several inches of fine dry snow covering their sleeping bags. This added one more chore: to remove as much snow as possible before attempting to warm the cabin.

When the sun quit rising above the hills to the south, the days all blended together. The strength of the wind marked the days in memory. If there were a calm day, it stood out like a national holiday.

The long nights were filled with wild dream excursions. Both Tim and Loretta returned to their early childhoods and relived the memorable as well as the not-so-clear experiences that now seemed to be important. It surprised them both to be going back in time instead of venturing into the future.

It was getting colder by the day. Mantra's thin Lab coat just couldn't keep up. He begged and whined until he was allowed into a warm sleeping bag. Even a large fire didn't warm the hut enough to be comfortable. If they were doing chores such as splitting wood or hauling water, the cold was almost tolerable. Within minutes of resting, however, there was only one warm and safe place to be—back in the bag.

Neither one had to say it, but both knew that this was getting much tougher than they had expected. Every peaceful moment was hard-earned. Food supplies were dangerously low. A wolf pack left a half-devoured moose cow just over the bluff after Tim had shot over their heads to scare them off. Mantra's menu was set. Tim and Loretta were sticking to their vegetarian diet, which now consisted of rationed bowls of watery granola each morning washed down with rosehip tea, *if* they could get the water to boil, which depended on how hard the wind was blowing.

Sprouts raised in small canisters was the main course each evening. It was Tim's job to keep them warm. He lay curled up in his sleeping bag with the sprout farm tightly tucked against his bare chest.

The lack of food, light and heat was taking its toll. Tim was running out of steam. Raising sprouts was the best he could do; even meditating seemed to take too much energy.

Loretta was scared. She had never been this thin, and she couldn't get warm unless she was snowshoeing at a fast pace. Breaking a sweat could be fatal at this stage, so she balanced her efforts on a fine line.

They weren't sure how far it was to Tanana, which they guessed was directly south over the bare hills. After much discussion, they both agreed they would never make it even ten miles. They had waited too long. Loretta didn't say it, but she felt she might be able to reach the village. Her main fear was what she would find when she returned with help.

Each morning Loretta stomped out H-E-L-P in the flat ground above their hut. She would then drag the wind-blown willow branches from the sign she had built the day before onto the new letters.

This not only kept her warm, but also gave a ray of hope. They were on no inter-village flight paths; the only airplanes seen were at about forty thousand feet leaving a vapor trail.

Loretta knew if she gave up and stayed in her bag all day, it would soon be over. Each morning brought just enough renewed hope and energy to rebuild her plea for help.

They hardly talked now. Tim was in a daze. He was convinced that the large gray wolf which often stuck its head in through their canvas door during the early morning hours was just waiting for the scent of death. Loretta didn't see it that way. She felt there was concern in those large, yellow eyes only inches away from the opening in her mummy bag.

Sometime in March the northern caribou herd moved down into the Tozitna Valley. Don Kratzer, a village school teacher, and Alfred Miller left the short, snowpacked Tanana airstrip to go have a look from Don's Maule. After one hour they had covered most of the lower Tozitna, and Don decided to continue upriver even though the turbulence was getting worse. After several more miles of being tossed about, Don decided he had better turn back. As the small plane banked to the right in a shallow turn, Alfred squinted to focus on a blur of movement on the next bench upriver. He quickly tapped hard on Don's left shoulder, indicating a request to turn that direction. Don rolled the wings back to the left. Now they could both see the tiny figure waving two handfuls of willow branches.

It took five passes before Don finally set the ski plane down on the windblown, crusty, washboard flat next to the willow sign. The little lady on snowshoes ran up and hugged the pilot before she said a word. Alfred, a Native Alaska Eskimo, could not believe how this couple had lived. Tim's sleeping bag had frozen to the floor inside the hut and was glazed over like a scene from *Dr. Zhivago*. When they helped Tim up to get prepared for the flight, Alfred stared, thinking, "He's built like a bicycle frame with long-johns on." Alfred had never seen anyone so thin.

After ten days in the small Tanana hospital, Tim's feet were saved and Loretta could hold down a regular diet. Everyone wanted to get a look at this mystery couple who had barely survived a winter in what the local Athabascans called the "Valley of the Raven."

Tim and Loretta made friends with Mr. Day, the hospital administrator. He offered to help find possible income, as they were completely destitute now. It didn't take long. One phone call to another administrator and Tim and Loretta were soon working at the village school, teaching fifth and sixth graders what they needed to know about survival in the wilderness.

I would have liked to see the Indian kids' faces during the class on raising sprouts by using belly heat while curled up in a sleeping bag. Or better yet, their parents' looks that evening when they heard about the latest in Arctic wilderness survival technique.

Mert

In the few months I'd been living in Tanana, I heard many stories about the old-timer Mert Attwood. He lived in the small cabin on Front Street overlooking the river next to Coghill's shop. I arrived in December, and, due to an exceptionally cold November, Mert had locked up and gone visiting in the Lower 48. The more stories I heard, the sooner I hoped to meet this Alaska pioneer. At one year old, Mert had come to Alaska in 1906 to be with his father Harold, one of the original settlers of the mining community of Fox, just north of Fairbanks. When Mert was nineteen he saw the first airplane fly in the state. Later he was taught to fly by both Sig and Noel Wien. He went on to mine many of the creeks from the Canadian border to Nome.

After an extra long winter, it was finally April and the river ice was ready to go out. The only road in town was almost dry.

I was working evening shift at the village hospital when a loud rumbling out front made me think the river ice must be moving. I pushed open the heavy, metal hospital door; a giant, yellow piece of heavy equipment was idling only a few feet away at the base of the stairs.

A thick head of white hair rooted atop a big, barrel-chested man came around the front of the loader bucket. He walked into the lobby. Even inside the lobby, the machinery was drowning out any conversation I tried to begin.

The old-timer went into the hall and said in a mumbling tone, "I need a nurse."

I informed him that I was the nurse. He cocked his head sideways and gave me one of those "be serious" looks.

"Yes, I'm the evening nurse."

He hesitantly gave me his arm to check his blood pressure. I assured him that 140/80 was OK. He then introduced himself as Mert Attwood and shook my hand, squeezing most of the blood back up to my elbow for a few seconds.

I escorted Mert to the front door. I had a definite feeling that he wasn't going to stop by on evening shift again until he was sure there was a real (female) nurse on duty.

Mert grabbed the handrail, hoisted himself up the ladder and into the cab of the huge machine. When I recorded his blood pressure later in his chart, I was surprised to learn that the man was 72 years old.

Mert was always moving: hauling gravel in a 1952 flatbed, plowing dirt with his 350 Caterpillar tractor, working the front-end loader. His hair stayed in place, and his clothes remained spotless. Mert seemed to be the one doing most of the work in the village.

I would stop by to visit on summer evenings while Mert worked on his big equipment. Slowly we grew to be friends, although he didn't talk much. When Mert told a story, he remembered every detail as far back as 1915.

The following winter Mert boarded up the cabin again, locked his shop doors and headed for Las Vegas with the Alaska Pioneers.

But on the first warm spring day, from the raised porch of the post office I saw Mert's yellow loader rocking its way down River Street.

As I stepped back out into the sunlight, I saw Mert's bright white hair through the thick glass of the loader cab. Sitting beside him was a small lady, glowing with blonde hair and pearls strung around her neck.

Mert beamed a wide smile as he stepped down. I walked over to greet him and welcome him back to town. He waved to the lady up in the cab, "Come on down, Teddy." A spry lady hopped down to meet me.

As I walked towards the hospital, I thought this was happiness at its best. Mert had found a lady who enjoyed riding with him in his loader.

Reverend Keller enjoyed telling how he first met Mert. It was minus forty degrees. At dinner one evening, there was a knock on the front door of the Mission house. The Reverend pulled the stiff, frosted door open. There was big Mert in his coveralls, waving his hands and saying in short, breathless spurts, "Rev, please, I need some water!"

"Wow!" the Rev thought, "Mert must have swallowed a hot tamale."

Then he saw the flames reflected in the porch windows. Mert's oil truck looked like a giant candle, as the long, yellow flames waved from the top of the truck.

Reverend Keller ran to the kitchen sink, hoping the water pressure was up. Meanwhile, slipping his boots on, he grabbed the bucket of tea-colored water and came racing to the front door. Mert and the burning truck were gone!

Reverend Keller ran into the street, just in time to see a yellow streak go around the corner, heading for the airport.

Mert had decided the fire wasn't going to be easy to put out, so he raced for the gravel airstrip downriver on the west end of town. He thought that if it was going to blow up, he had better get it out of the village. The flames pointed backwards as the truck raced through the village. Mert was power shifting, pushing the old tanker to its maximum speed. He pulled alongside the runway, turned off the key and jumped from the running board of the still rolling truck. Much to Mert's surprise, he had actually blown the fire out.

Over the next few years Mert telephoned several times to ask if I might know where he could buy a small sports car, like a Datsun 280 Z. I just couldn't see Mert in such a little car. He then explained how he hadn't seen one before he squashed it with the dump truck, and now he had to replace it.

One afternoon Mert called to see if I knew where he could buy a door for a Lincoln Continental. He explained that that morning he didn't see a train coming. It hit him from the side and dragged him almost a mile before the train finally stopped.

In Anchorage there are several strategically located corner telephone poles, better known as "Mert's pivot poles." They have large chunks missing a foot and a half up from the base. These poles were used by Mert to help him make a corner while driving his long, Lowboy tractor trailer. Mert would often cut the corner a little tight; the trailer would jump the curb, scrape the pole, then pivot around the turn and only God could help anything in the way.

Mert spent his latter years in Anchorage with Teddy. Each spring, though, he would gear up to go look over some new gold claims that he had been dreaming about all winter. Much to her dismay, Teddy's yard was filled with Mert's mining equipment. In his spare time, Mert volunteered his equipment and built the road to the Palmer Transportation Museum. The park was later named in his honor.

At eighty-four and after several small strokes, Mert was moved into a nursing home. I visited whenever I could get to Anchorage.

The last time I saw Mert alive, he still had a sparkle in his eye and talked of going to check out new ground around Livengood.

Whiskey

Whiskey had run in the first Iditarod race with Sandy Hamilton's team. He was a "river dog," part husky and part Heinz 57 mutt. His short, powerful legs put him in big demand, especially for the mountainous first half of the race. Whiskey ran in wheel position. His job was to keep the sled and driver out of the spruce gullies and open streams. When Sandy and team had reached the flat, frozen Yukon, a little over halfway, Whisky was too slow. The team needed more speed, so Sandy dropped him in the village of Ruby.

Now fourteen and semi-retired in my dog yard, Whiskey worked his own hours as a stud. He was a strong, hardworking dog with real character. I wanted to keep his bloodlines in the team.

The last dog trip that spring, we took five teams out to visit Stan and Helen's homestead, forty miles north on the Tozitna River. As we harnessed up the teams, Whiskey howled, begging to come along. Margaret was a soft touch, and, since her team was the slowest, she offered to let him pull wheel for her.

At Stan's that evening, she told me about Whiskey's failing hind legs. He was stiff, even in the warm April sun. Each time the team took a break on the trip out, Whiskey had more and more difficulty getting started. We all hated the thought that Whiskey's time might have come. I had been putting off the obvious for almost a year. Now this trip had taken its toll on him.

After a two-day visit, I planned to drive Stan's snowmachine with a loaded sled back to town. The others would take off early with the teams, and I would catch up later with the snowmachine. Whiskey was my dog; I knew it was my job to send him on to doggie heaven.

After drinking at least ten cups of tea, I finally walked out to Stan's empty dog yard. Whiskey jumped up, putting his front paws on my chest, his face inches from mine. He gave me that "How ya doing, buddy?" look. I cringed. I'm not big on shooting anything, except pool and maybe a crap game now and then. The thought of actually shooting my first and favorite dog was something that I had never let close to my mind.

Staring into those big, yellow, wolf-like eyes, I made a quick deal with Whiskey. He could run behind the snowmachine, free of harness. I even promised to take it slow. I hoped his hips would hang in there and he could make it home.

Three miles out from Stan's cabin I stopped up on the flats to look back. Whiskey was fifty yards behind, his tongue flopping side to side, his short, rapid steps moving him along at his old Iditarod pace. He didn't slow a step as he caught up and leaped onto the snowmachine, straddled the seat, and gave me a "Thanks for stopping; I was getting tired of this running behind ya" look.

The old Stud rode the next thirty-seven miles home, scrunching me forward and trying to take over the narrow seat. When we pulled in late that evening, all the teams were already bedded down at the house. Margaret and friends were making dinner. There was a cheer and applause as I came into the house. I had no way of knowing there was a running bet. It seemed everybody knew that Whiskey would get to ride home on the snowmachine with me, and there was no way I was going to shoot that old dog.

Over the next two years Whiskey fathered many pups. Several went on to run in Stan Zuray's 1983 Iditarod team. It was a sad time when Whiskey—that 100 per cent sled dog, Mr. Personality—finally went to check out that big milk bone in the sky.

Part II

Over the Tundra

Zippy

Dave was flying his Cessna 152 extra low while following the Tanana River into Fairbanks. The heavy rain made forward visibility just about zilch. Dave could see better out the side window, so he kept his eyes on the river bank, judging his altitude by the big spruce trees.

The huge rivers of interior Alaska have saved many a pilot flying the bush. "When the weather comes down, you find a river and stick with it" is often the first advice given a cheechako pilot. Trees and mountains don't usually pop up in the middle of a river, and *if* you have to put down, a sand bar can be much more comfortable than being wedged into a stand of trees or inverted on the bumpy tundra.

All these thoughts racing through Dave's mind tried to make him feel better about flying twenty feet above one of the most winding rivers in the world. Spruce branches were just feet off his left wingtip.

After what seemed like hours, Coghill's fuel depot and the village of Nenana appeared in a blur on the right river bank. Whew! Dave was glad to see some piece of civilization, then he cringed: What had happened to the Nenana bridge and that set of power lines? He couldn't believe he hadn't even seen them!

He was lucky to have been flying low enough that they didn't slow him down.

When Dave saw the last cabin on the south edge of town, he breathed a sigh of relief. The fog was getting thicker, but there were no more big obstacles between him and Fairbanks.

Zippy, Dave's little curly-haired mutt, sat up on the right seat. Ears pointed, Zippy was studying the river bank out his side window. He always rode along with Dave and was fearless. If Dave had to land and fight off a grizzly bear, Zippy would be his first choice out of all ten sled dogs in his yard.

Nothing fazed Zippy. Ever.

Dave tried to keep his left tire approximately twenty feet off the water. He rolled the small plane slightly into the next curve.

Suddenly, in clear view straight ahead and less than one hundred feet away, Dave looked into the faces of a crowd of people on the deck of the riverboat *Discovery*. A hard jerk back planted the yoke into Dave's rib cage. The plane jumped straight up, the tourists ducked.

The plane's wheels just missed the exhaust stack of the big, slow sternwheeler. Dave knew he had pulled too hard. The tiny plane hung pointing straight up. He pushed the throttle to full power and nosed over, praying the plane wouldn't stall and fall into the river.

When the events of the past ten seconds hit home, Dave's knees starting shaking so hard he could hear them clicking.

So much for the it's-safer-over-the-river theory. Nobody ever mentioned riverboats.

The rest of the trip seemed to take all day. Dave tried to relax. He looked over and asked, "Zippy, did you see that?" It was obvious Zippy had: The sad, little dog lay head down on the floor.

If it scared Zippy, it was bad.

It was never easy to get Zippy back into the plane, no matter how high Dave promised to fly!

Merton J. Attwood, first airplane ride, Fairbanks, Alaska, 1926.

Mert with one of his favorite Bush planes, the Gullwing V-77, 1986.

Lee Edwin, Sr., my best man at our wedding, Tanana, Alaska, 1982. (Bottom: Lee with my son Christopher McCann.)

McCann's Roadhouse directly across from the confluence of the Yukon and Tanana rivers; one mile upriver from the village of Tanana.

Streisand, my first leader. Wow, could she howl!

The author in LB-30 (N92MK) before dismantling at Kalakakit Creek.

Kevin and Bill Sheldon removing midsection, Pat Kovach.

Back Row: Ann Wood, Lynda, Hans, Blackie, Russ.
Front Row: Fleming, Mike, Claire, Mert Attwood.

Fishwheel in front of McCann's Roadhouse
on the Yukon River.

Squashy (Ron Wilhouski) and "Pony" (good
friends).

Sean Gleason with new truck. ("Toothpaste")

Dr. Bill, Margaret (Irish Rose) O'Hallaran, Joe and Sherri Runyan with children Zedti and Zabeth, Mike McCann.

Andrew T. Bukovinsky
June 1947 — September 1968

Dr. Bill

Late one afternoon, Dr. Bill putted overhead in his newly purchased, yellow and blue, T-Craft floatplane. He rocked the wings when he saw us cutting fish at the tables on the beach below.

At 8 p.m., the late sun was shining from the west through the thick cottonwoods. Alex, Sean and I sat drinking tea at the long table in the front window.

The dogs began barking. I thought there must be a bear heading for the fish rack. Then a person appeared, running up the short trail in a flurry of motion. It was Bill's wife Margaret. She was waving her arms wildly, swatting at a thick cloud of mosquitoes.

I met her at the side door. She was cussing a streak in her thick Irish brogue. She looked haggard, and while she tried to catch her breath I asked if she had been in the plane with Bill earlier. She nodded.

Envisioning the worst, we all peered out at the river to make sure there were no plane pieces floating by.

Margaret was excited. She barely made sense, but it seemed she was fine, just a bit ticked off.

She slowed down. "Yeah, Bill couldn't get the bird off the water. He was so embarrassed. We tried and tried. The plane would roar, then nose up and drag the tail in the river. We tried for miles."

Margaret went on to explain how they taxied six miles downriver, hoping the current and a breeze would help pick the small plane up. But the evening was calm, and the only way Bill had gotten the plane to take off earlier in front of the village was with a stiff afternoon breeze.

As they drifted into the curve just above Tanana, Margaret told Bill to taxi for shore. Here she climbed out onto the float and, after the propeller stopped, leaped to shore. She then shoved the T-Craft back into the current. She wanted Bill to go ahead and visit friends at the fish camps upriver, knowing he only had two days off from the clinic. She also hoped to save him the embarrassment of taxiing back into town. My house was just above the village and her first stop.

Margaret was awfully good-hearted. She exclaimed the only things she would have done differently would have been to let Bill taxi her closer to town and to have brought bug dope.

"Oh well," she added, "he's so tickled with his new plane. Now if he could just learn to take off with the *two* of us in it."

B-24

Bill Sheldon phoned to ask if I had a couple days to help him get a B-24 out of the brush. I wasn't quite sure what type of plane he was after. Bill explained that it was a big old World War II four-engine bomber. When I heard that, I signed on immediately.

We loaded his Cessna 206 on a sunny June afternoon with the usual survival gear—beans to bullets—jumped in and headed north. Four hours later, we touched down on an abandoned White Alice site runway which straddled the top of a mountain. The area, known as Kalakakit Creek, is ten miles south of Galena. The windsock pole at the edge of the old gravel strip leaned at a forty-five degree angle. Only a few shreds of a disintegrated sock waved in the breeze. This was serious evidence that strong winds whipped through this area occasionally. Bill circled several times. We quickly spotted the remains of the huge albatross of an airplane that had been dragged down the hillside into the brush many years ago.

When we landed and climbed out of the 206, the mosquitoes were glad to see us. Trying to find that winged dinosaur on the ground took awhile. We walked down the south face of the mountain in ten-foot high alders, our bear rifles in hand. I began to think it might have been a mirage. Bill lit a cigar and squinted. A small patch of aluminum reflected a ray of sun through the thick brush. We waddled through the lumpy undergrowth up to the giant B-24. It was full of bullet holes, and much of its skin looked like a giant cheese grater. There it squatted, like a large, wounded goose that held its wings out to stay above the brush.

After walking across the seventy-foot wing section, I thought the only other thing I had ever been on that felt as sturdy was the Brooklyn Bridge. We nodded at each other several times without saying a word. We were both thinking the same thing: "Sure is big!"

The engines were gone, salvaged along with many other parts years ago. Much of the damage on the old bird appeared to have been done after the crash. A D-8 Caterpillar had dragged her backwards three hundred yards down the hillside.

Drilling the thousands of half-inch rivets that held the wing section to the fuselage was going to take awhile. We hustled back to Bill's plane to unload the small gas compressor with several new rolls of air hose. There were large piles of bear scat on the runway. It appeared that if the bugs didn't get us the bears would.

The first few rivets told me it might be a long summer. Even with the new drill bits, each rivet seemed to take hours.

Reinforcements arrived late that afternoon. Bill's son Kevin and his two friends, Pat and Kurt, arrived in a chartered plane. After assessing the damage and seeing the size of the rivets we were drilling, Kevin pulled out a sharpened air chisel. He experimented, attempting not to damage the skin while knocking the heads off these bridge-sized rivets. Kevin quickly refined his technique, and soon there were dime-sized chunks of rivet rapid-firing off the wing.

This plane, better known as N92MK, was refurbished after the war. The outer wing panel and stabilizer were beefed up; four new Pratt and Whitney engines were mated to the Liberator (B-24). When the aircraft emerged, it was virtually a C-87 Liberator Express Transport.

Brought to Alaska by Morrison-Knudsen Construction Co. in 1957, N92MK hauled nearly two-and-a-half million pounds of cargo in Alaska during its first nine months. It flew mostly to remote radar warning sites under construction.

In the late Fifties, the end for N92MK came when it dragged a wheel in a snow bank on landing at Kalakakit Creek. That rough landing sprung the fuselage out of alignment. The airplane was scavenged clean, then dragged backwards down the south slope to the dump.

Years later, the Aviation Museum in Anchorage received title and sold the rights to an entrepreneur in Florida. He must have had a few extra bucks to start a war plane collection.

Our job was to get the old bird into pieces. We then had to haul her to the small gravel strip so a large C-133 freighter could come in and take her to Anchorage.

Dismantling was going well. With the four of us popping rivets, the nose became separated. Then we blocked up the heavy wing so we could cut away the fuselage. The wing was solid and indestructible. We knew we would have to move it as one piece.

The only vehicle running at the remote site was an Air Force 6x6 that could barely pull itself up the hillside. We had to find a way to get the heavy pieces moved.

During a short reconnaissance hike to the radar site on the mountain top, we found a D-8 Cat and a road grader abandoned when the site was closed ten years before. The steering was gone from the grader and the Cat was basically stripped. It took two days of "Rube Goldberg-ing" parts and a flight in the 206 to Galena to borrow a set of large batteries. We were able to get the grader running with Mickey Mouse steering and no brakes. It made for a wild ride off the mountain and through the brush to our work site.

In one busy, hot, buggy afternoon we had the old Liberator in pieces, sitting on the side of the runway, ready to be airmailed to Anchorage.

The last time I visited the museum on Lake Hood, there was N92MK still a large pile of parts stacked out back that looked much worse than when we found her in the brush. Luckily, I specialize only in taking things apart.

Jerry

Jerry was tall. I never realized how tall until I tried to squeeze him into my small PA-12. We were flying the Iditarod race, keeping an eye on our musher friend Joe Runyan.

After leaving Anchorage, we followed the many large dog teams strung out on the race trail from Big Lake to Skwentna. Suddenly a large, gray cloud engulfed the airplane. I turned fast toward the north and, hopefully, toward cleaner air. Over the radio I soon learned that Mt. Spur had just blown its top. I decided that instead of trying to return to Anchorage, we would attempt to fly to Talkeetna.

When we arrived at Talkeetna, I circled the state airport. Black pavement was showing through on most of the runway. My plane was rigged with skis, and bare pavement is not conducive to good ski landing. The flight service attendant suggested we land at the old airstrip in town, which was snow-covered, short, narrow and ended abruptly at the Fairview Inn.

We were heavily loaded. I carried a lot of power and trimmed full nose down. We circled several times. The ash cloud was close behind; I knew I had to land.

On approach, the tail felt as if it would quit flying any second. To avoid instant catastrophe, I pushed the stick forward and kept the air speed high. We came in over the river and touched down moving fast. The temperature was thirty degrees, making the ski strip extra slick. I chopped the power and dropped the flaps, but we didn't slow down. I kept pulling the stick back, trying to jam the tail wheel into the snow. It was too icy and hard packed. Down both sides of the runway were parked planes. If we made it between those, there was a big, white lodge—the Fairview Inn—waiting at the runway's end. I tried not to panic as we seemed to pick up speed.

A telephone pole stood to the left of our path, fifty feet before the lodge. I thought, "If we don't stop in time, I'll smack the left wing on that pole, spin around and maybe then avoid hitting the lodge."

Half way down the runway, the propeller finally stopped, but we were still sliding along at a rapid rate. Jerry recognized our predicament. I turned just enough to see him scrunching down with his arms clamped to the tubing above his head. He was pushing himself down as low as he could. I barely heard him, but what I did catch was him mimicking a southern drawl, "Guess who's comin' tuh dinnah? Guess who's comin' tuh dinnah?"

I laughed, but at this point I knew that if we missed the pole, Jerry and I were going through the front window of the Fairview Inn just in time for dinner. When I had given up all hope, the tail wheel started to dig in and I could feel a bit of drag.

We stopped barely twenty feet before the pole. From there I could see several smiling faces in the front window of the lodge. We spent that afternoon visiting around the community. By now the volcanic ash had moved north, assuring us we were going to be in Talkeetna for a few days listening to the Iditarod on the radio. We stayed at the Fairview Inn that night and enjoyed a few beers with the locals. They already knew that I had almost hit THE POLE that afternoon. Cliff Hudson, a local flying legend, very considerately let us know that we wouldn't have been the first. I went out and saw the paint chips and the confetti-size fabric strips hanging from its splintered runway-facing side.

The ash had stopped all air traffic following the race. The dogs kept going, leaving news crews and the Iditarod air force behind. Volcanic ash can destroy an engine in minutes. After being delayed two days, it was a big relief to fly through the pass and hit the wide-open Kuskokwim area.

When Joe Runyan and team pulled into the McGrath checkpoint that evening, he saw Jerry and me standing to the side. With a wide grin he asked where we had been. Jerry answered, "We were back in Talkeetna. Mike was thinking about buying the Fairview Inn."

It turned into quite a race that year. A big storm hit the front racers between McGrath and Flat. Then it cleared, and the temperature dropped to minus fifty degrees at Anvik on the Yukon. Another storm held up the racers on the coast for several days. After eight days on the trail, Jerry questioned how much further the race was. I told him we only had two hundred more miles and it would be over. During the trip, he often shook his head slowly and said, "This is a dream come true. We are camping out in Alaska in the winter."

That first clear morning in Unalakleet, Jerry and I got the plane heated and dug out of a drift on the river. We headed for Nome, flying the coast trail. We waved our wing tip at the leading mushers—Swenson, Butcher, Buser and Runyan—who were now getting close to Elim.

Tucked back off the windswept coast, White Mountain was a welcome sight. We circled the river landing strip. I knew if we landed, it would surely be for the night and maybe much longer the way the weather changes on the coast. I elected to continue the seventy miles into Nome. Then, if possible, I would borrow a snowmachine to backtrack and meet the racers on the trail the next day.

We barely made it into Nome. A wall of hellish wind hit when we were twenty miles out. It suddenly became so rough I thought the wings were about to leave us. I was tempted to turn back for White Mountain when Nome came clearly into sight. I clenched my teeth and focused on keeping the PA-12 upright.

The city airstrip never looked so good. We finally taxied behind two tractor trailer vans. We used every last inch of rope to secure the plane in what turned out to be one of the severest storms I had ever witnessed in Alaska.

At Iditarod headquarters concern was mounting for all the racers on the coastal trail. Advice over the ham radios was for the racers to stay at the checkpoints. A whiteout with minus wind chill factors can be deadly to a musher.

Pressure was on the front teams. This was the year of the showdown between Swenson and Butcher, and several other good teams were right on their tails into White Mountain.

Due to whiteout conditions on the treeless coast, many hoped the racers would sit tight. With only seventy miles remaining out of the thousand forty-nine, Rick Swenson and Martin Buser decided to give it a shot, trail or no trail. Tim Osmar, Joe Runyan and Susan Butcher decided too much was at stake. They turned their teams back ten miles out of White Mountain to the protected checkpoint.

The storm wailed. News was that Swenson and Buser were unaccounted for on the trail between Topkok Hills and Safety Roadhouse. Search parties were dispatched.

From the comfort of a friend's cabin in Nome, Jerry and I listened through the crackle and static of the local radio to the frequent updates on which mushers were in and out of the many checkpoints. Jerry had caught the Iditarod fever. I felt lucky to have shared this trip with a good friend who really loved Alaska.

Jerry was from North Philadelphia. At his peak, he stood a hair from six foot eight inches. He said Wilt Chamberlain was the only one in the neighborhood taller when he was a kid. Jerry spent thirty years working for the Philly power company, climbing high tension power poles. Jerry had just turned sixty. With his healthy, African-bronze skin, he looked more like forty.After retiring, he came to Alaska. He was like a kid in a candy store.

The next fall Jerry went to Nepal to hike in the Himalayas with an Elderhostel group. I received a call from his cousin Olga. She told me Jerry had gotten altitude sickness and didn't make it off the mountain. I couldn't believe it.

I am convinced that Jerry picked his place and time. He loved the mountains, and they don't come any bigger than the Himalayas. In my book, they don't come any bigger or better than Jerry either.

Honeymoon Ride

Doug and Anna were familiar with most of the landable beaches and ridges spanning from Nuka Island off the Kenai Peninsula to Nome on the Bering Sea.

Since Doug met his German partner Anna, he rarely landed on a civilized runway. Half the year his Super Cub was rigged with fiberglass skis. During the warmer months he mounted dune‑buggy-sized tundra tires underneath, which made it possible for Doug to land on the roughest terrain without flipping over. Landing on a paved runway was like a walk in the park for Doug.

Often, Anna would slink her long frame into the back seat of the narrow Super Cub, then Doug would grab the overhead tubing and pull himself up onto the pilot seat. With cross-country skis inside and two pairs of babiche snowshoes strapped to the struts, they would head out to the Interior to hike and ski the ridges of the Tozitna and Melozitna valleys.

In the summer they aimed for the Seward Peninsula where they scanned the riverbeds for good sandbars on which to land and from which to dip their hubcap-sized gold pans.

It was now early fall—cold at night, bright and sunny during the shortening days. There wasn't enough snow in the mountains yet to warrant putting skis on the airplane.

Doug decided to take a flight and look for mountain goats. After fueling up the Cub, he folded the wing and engine covers, stashing them neatly on the front seat of his old Ford pickup. He and Anna flew along the high, narrow ridges of Kenai Fjord Park on the south side of Kachemak Bay. In the clear, cold air, the snow-white goats could be seen for miles against the dark, shale slopes.

"Few words can convey what it feels like to be eye-to-eye with these amazing animals while they stand on razor-edge perches,"Anna thought. She hoped her camera would be able to capture the essence.

A flat, narrow saddle on the ridge was just too nice to pass by. Doug circled and looked it over closely. Dinner plate-sized rocks covered the small, potential airstrip.

Doug cut the power, then pulled the flap handle three notches. The big tires touched down softly as the plane rocked back and forth, weaving slightly side to side. "Like landing on two beach balls," Doug thought. Then the Cub pulled to the right. Doug gave it hard left rudder and added more power to stay up on the flat of the narrow strip. He thought, "It shouldn't be pulling this hard. Maybe the right brake is sticking." Doug rocked the control stick and added more power to try and pivot the plane. It wouldn't go! Doug pulled the mixture knob to shut off the fuel supply to the engine. The prop slowly quit spinning.

Swinging his right leg out, he noticed the ground seemed a little closer than it had when he'd climbed in back in Homer.

Immediately the problem was obvious. The right tire bulged at the bottom. Doug kneeled down and could see a slice in the sidewall. It was long enough to slide his hand into.

The right wing dipped radically from where they stopped to look back at the plane, one hundred yards away.

Anna was concerned but confident Doug would think of a cure; he always did.

They continued walking along the ridge to see how close they could get to the group of goats for a photo opportunity. A cold breeze persisted.

The family of moss munchers seemed to be posing for a portrait as Anna crouched, crawled and clicked away with her Nikon camera. Their thick, white coats glowed in the evening light.

The fall sun was sinking fast. They headed back to the wounded plane.

Doug had an idea. They collected armfuls of moss from the hillside and packed it a hundred yards to the ridgetop.

Doug stuck a 4-inch flat rock into the sliced tire, twisting it sideways. The hole opened enough to stuff handfuls of the spongy moss inside.

Anna pushed up on the right wing to take weight off the flat tire. When Doug finished stuffing the goat food into the split, Anna let the wing down and the tire went flat again.

It was too far to shuttle enough moss, as daylight was getting short.

Doug didn't like the idea of trying to take off from such a narrow ridge with the tire pulling the plane so strongly to the right.

Anna had an idea. She took off her down vest, wadded it into a ball, and handed it to Doug. He got the picture and began stuffing the vest into the tire. His own Carhartt coat came next. It was making a difference.

If only he had brought the wing covers, his clothes wouldn't be in such demand. He mumbled, adding a few expletives as he undid his blue chamois shirt. It went in easy. One thing led to another. Soon down to his Fruit of the Looms, Doug thought of the sprint he would have to make from the plane to the hangar. He decided to keep them on. Anna understood the look clearly.

She began peeling layers off, as Doug shivered, shook and jumped around as if he were making a mountaintop aerobic exercise video. Now down to her skivvies, Doug held the wing up as Anna began stuffing.

The plane did well leaving the strip. After leveling off, Doug glanced back at Anna. She had her arms folded across her chest. He had to grin, although he was even more visible with the Plexiglas float-style door to his right.

It was a particularly cool flight.

Doug planned to land and taxi fast to his hangar if the stuffed tire could handle it. Anna hoped their entire wardrobe wouldn't spray out onto the runway as the plane touched down.

An ERA Twin Otter was at the warm-up ramp directly in Doug's route to parking. Doug guided the lame Cub off the runway and swung a wide turn almost wingtip to wingtip around the commercial aircraft. Anna sank as low as possible in her seat.

The Otter was full, faces in every window. The pilot did a double-take.

Doug heard a voice over the radio, "Hey, Super Cub, a little cool to be flying around buck naked." There was silence. Then the microphone clicked on again, "Are you on your honeymoon?"

Part III

Back on the Hudson

No Pets

The rule "No Pets" was on the top of the list for families moving into the new projects.

We had been living in the old projects during which time my sister Mary had made friends with Tripod, a three-legged, one-eyed hound. I often brought home hurt ducks, squirrels, and even a lame Canadian goose from the local park. Our mother did her best to help repair the wounded critters we found.

Now we were selected from the list of the many growing families who needed larger apartments. Mom was excited but a bit concerned as she read the list of rules loudly to my three sisters and me.

"No Pets" was first, and she repeated it three times. The brand new apartment was thick with the scent of linoleum glue and fresh paint. It even had a third bedroom and a large closet for storing our bikes so we wouldn't have to lock them to a pole outside.

The front window was only feet from a four-lane highway, which added drag racing and pile-ups to our nightly entertainment.

I planned to slowly ease Mom up on the "No Pets" rule. First I brought home a hamster that had crawled into my pocket at Newberry's Pet Store. He lasted only a couple of weeks. He could have been with us longer, but he kept sticking his head through the cage's narrow bars. He would chew on anything he could reach. His cheeks would puff up until he couldn't pull his fat face back into the cage, often for hours.

Mom said she couldn't stand the sight of his flared face stuck in the bars. She tried pulling him back in by his hind legs, which only made his face swell up more. Mary soon found a classmate to take "Cheeky" the hamster.

One morning during Sister Daniel Mary's Catechism class, I was seated in the back row reading an old *Boy's Life* magazine. There was a small picture advertisement of a stuffed raccoon and a large wolf. The ad was for a mail-order taxidermy class.

Something in my brain clicked: If I couldn't have live pets, maybe I could have a stuffed one.

That evening I turned my paper route change into a five dollar bill at the local Portuguese deli. On the way to school the next morning, I mailed off my order to N.W. School of Taxidermy in Omaha, Nebraska, not mentioning a word to anyone.

After what seemed like months, the school packet finally arrived. It was a series of ten lessons. A new booklet would arrive each month.

Cool and sunny, it was now fall. On my two-mile walk from school, I kept an eye out for dead critters. It seemed when you least needed one, even in New York, they were lying everywhere—dead squirrels, pigeons, dogs, even a raccoon on a rare day.

I didn't spot a thing for several days. Then one afternoon on the last stretch of my hike, I saw next to the curb a gray, fluffy tail moving in the breeze.

My heart sped up as I neared my possible new friend. It looked like most road kills—as flat as a homemade potholder. I grabbed the squirrel's tail, hoping it wouldn't snap off. I had to tug a bit to get the flattened body free from the highway.

It fit nicely between the books in my bookbag, which I knew was the only way I would get the squirrel up to my room. I set him under the bed, next to the radiator to help dry him out a bit more. I studied up on my next move.

It's amazing how things can fall together. Within a week there were two more flattened squirrels and a muskrat under my bed. I studied the list of procedures over and over. The manual didn't have a way to unflatten the critters. I used my own inventiveness, however, and decided to soak them in warm water for a couple of days under my bed.

The soaking helped; some of the blood washed out, but it was still hard to tell what was what. The manual instructed me to start skinning from the hind legs. Luckily the tails were still attached to help orient me to which end was which. Half a card table worked great for stretching and tacking the small hides down, like was shown in the manual. Step two instructed me to cover the skin side with salt.

I rushed downstairs before Mom got home, and I grabbed the first can of white stuff from the cabinet. The little hides covered in the fine, white powder looked so clean tacked out on the card table. Then I slid the board back under the bed.

The next day was sunny and warm, a beautiful day. I ran most of the way home.

Mom definitely wasn't happy when she met me at the door. The fact that she didn't say a word but just pointed up the stairs to my bedroom as she clenched her teeth was kind of a giveaway.

My first thought was, "Maybe they came alive! A miracle! I believe!"

Halfway up the stairs, I could see the towels stuffed along the outside bottom of my door. Then came her loud voice, "I just can't believe the bloody mess you have under your bed! Next time you take half a bag of sugar and dump it on dead animals, you are going to see the priest!"

My room was covered with a thin layer of pink, sticky fluid. The sugar must have pulled the blood from the small skins. I was ordered immediately to throw my new little friends out the window.

I felt bad. In a sad tone I yelled back down the stairs, "First they get run over by who knows how many cars, then you make me throw them out the window!"

Lighter than Air

Lunch during wrestling season was rarely worth mentioning. Salad, maybe a micro serving of Jell-O and half an orange were considered a full meal, according to our coach. He encouraged us to stick to the routine by saying, "Okay, just go ahead and eat. Then we'll all get to watch that animal in the next weight class flatten you like a pancake."

How that thought stuck, especially when I was about to bite into a big, greasy burger or a hunk of apple pie. I only had to miss one weigh-in to become a believer. Ten extra pounds doesn't sound like much until it's solid muscle and he's holding you down on your back.

Home at noon that Friday, I ate my salad slowly, enjoying each bite for minutes. I sucked the juice from every leaf of lettuce as though it were the last ice cube in hell.

Fruit for dessert; I aimed for the pantry.

What I saw was a mirage: I hardly dared take a second look at the double-layer cake with its bright icing glaciering onto the waxed paper.

The fruit bowl sat empty. I turned slowly; the cake was real. I stood staring. After thinking a minute, I couldn't remember the coach ever mentioning cake. He did say sweets, but if I scraped the icing off.... Besides, I quickly reasoned, cake is mostly air. That's why it rises, RIGHT? It made sense. He never mentioned cake because he thought none of us had the willpower to remove the icing first. He would be proud of me.

The sharp blade neared the creamy cover. My mouth watered; a tinge of guilt ran up my spine. Time seemed to stand still. The knife hovered.

Usually, Mom left a note if there were a treat for lunch. Maybe she just forgot this time, or maybe the girls had baked it as a surprise. I didn't want to ruin their plan, but I couldn't pass up such a find.

With a big, meat-cutting knife in each hand, I sliced and lifted the cake top off like the lid of a large cookie jar. Carefully, I placed the knives and the iced cake top on the paper next to the now-scalped cake. Two spoonfuls of the fluffy chocolate just weren't enough. Before I slowed down, I had dug a trench around a small pillar of cake in the center.

Reconstruction went well, although a bit shaky as I eased the blades from under the lid, praying the center of the cake would hold. A few final, very light touches and the cake looked just as I had found it.

After wrestling practice that evening, I ran home. From the porch I could see the table set with our best cloth. That meant it was an a occasion. I strained my memory as I opened the glass door and eased in. Mom turned from the stove and, noticing my perplexed look, said, "Uncle John is coming for dinner. It's his birthday, and I baked him his favorite cake."

Remembering the cake sent a chill through me. Then things got a little blurry as I staggered across the kitchen. Mom looked concerned and said, "You'd better start eating more. That wrestling diet is making you look pale."

Uncle John was second only to the Pope in our house. Recently ordained a Monsignor, we rarely saw him. Normally, I would be waiting for him at the door.

Dinner went well. Then it was time for the birthday dessert.

In a panic I decided my only choice was to put a small hole in the cake's side and give a mouse credit—a good idea just a little too late. Mom had beaten me to the pantry. She was lighting the one candle stuck in the cake's center.

We all sang "Happy Birthday." I tried to stretch it by adding several extra verses. Uncle John beamed his big, Irish smile and blew out the candle. Mom handed the long cake knife across the table. I held my breath as he went for the first slice. The cake collapsed like a stuck balloon! There was a long silence while everyone stared open-mouthed.

Thank God Uncle John had a sense of humor. The look Mom gave me only made me wish his sister were more like him!

Palm Sunday

Bobby and I had been building the fort in Grandma's backyard for several months. We had used everything from shopping carts to old doors and paint racks; we had almost everything we needed.

Palm Sunday we were up and dressed extra early for 6:00 Mass. Usually we went to the nine o'clock service, but this week we decided to go early. Church was just around the corner. We rushed home after Mass with our hands full of palms. We decided to return for a second load with the wagon.

In short order we filled the wagon with many of the palms from the vestibule of the church. Steadying the overloaded wagon through the alley, we rolled into Grandma's backyard. We spent the next two hours intently weaving a thatched roof for the top of the fort. It began to look like something from *National Geographic*. Needless to say, we were very proud of it.

Uncle John was the guest priest in the parish that week. He said nine o'clock Mass, which was the children's Mass. When he came home at 10:15, Mom said he was steaming. He couldn't believe it. He stomped around the kitchen with his collar undone and his face bright red. He ranted, "Somebody stole all the palms from the back of the church this morning. We had to splinter what was left into palm strings so everybody had something to take home. I just can't believe anybody could do such a thing!"

Mom said he was sipping on his coffee when he glanced out the back window of Grandma's house and then suddenly froze, like the day the earth stood still. Her gaze followed his, and she saw us up on the roof of our tree fort working diligently on the thatched roof. It didn't take us long to get the message when she came out. Mom helped us load that wagon full of palms. Again we went through the hole in the fence and down the alley towards the church.

The last thing I remember was her yelling loudly, but not clearly, "And if they ask you what your name is, you can't remember." It wasn't that easy being the Monsignor's nephew.

Skates

Whitney's pond was dimly lit, with a few skaters circling inside the plowed snow berms. We had recently moved into the neighborhood and often watched the skaters from afar. I was six, Mimi five, Mary four; to us, skating was something bigger kids did.

That evening, Mom was driving our old Chevy wagon over to Grandma's when we stopped at the red light on the corner.

Mimi, Mary and I stared down at the skaters. I rolled my window down to get a better view of the kids gliding along on the frozen pond. Mom told us several skating stories from her youth during the next three miles to Grandma's. It was hard to picture Mom on skates, especially now that she was about to deliver us a new sibling.

After the usual big dinner, I overheard Grandma telling Mom in the kitchen how she needed to get some bigger clothes. Mom's blouse was getting so tight that if a button let go, I was sure it would stun a squirrel at fifty feet. I stayed to her side as much as possible. After the lecture, I saw Grandma slip two bills into Mom's purse as we put on our coats to leave.

On our way home, Mom pulled up to the curb and stopped in front of McGrady's secondhand store. The thought of Mom in some moth-balled dress was not a happy one for me. "Lets go in and take a look," she said. My half asleep sisters shuffled in behind us.

This was one of my favorite places on the planet. After you got used to the musty mothball smell, there were all kinds of things to touch. Mr. McGrady met us at the door. He was an old, grumpy Irishmen with a big red nose and large tufts of white hair growing out of each ear. His giant belly looked like a ski jump from the side.

Mom had known him since she was a kid. They chatted as we roamed freely from the old fur coats to the stuffed birds and down the aisles of picture frames and old dishes. My favorite objects were the stuffed pheasants which looked so alive.

Mom ushered us to the back corner shelves of used ice skates. Within twenty minutes we all had our first pair.

I didn't want to take them off until Mr. McGrady explained the damage done by walking on concrete. I did try to sleep with them on that night, but Mom wouldn't have it. "You'll cut the sheets to shreds," she said very seriously.

We didn't miss a day of skating that winter. Mom was a good skater; she taught us something new each day until she delivered us a new sister, Susan.

Mom told us Grandma had given her the dollars for the skates. I never let on that I knew differently.

It's many years later now.

We are all damn good skaters and so are Mom's grandchildren Chris, Michael, Michelle and Kevin.

Toothpaste

Sean smiled as he proudly held up the keys to the old '52 Chevy pickup. He had just handed over seventy-five dollars of his pizza parlor wages to purchase his first automobile. The 25-year-old farm truck had been beefed up for heavy loads; this made it tilt forward at a steep angle, looking like a real hot rod!

I was invited for the test ride. Sean jumped in the driver's seat as I slowly slid in on the curb side. When Sean turned the key the truck sounded like half freight train and half cement mixer.

Sean nodded with a wide grin. After revving the rumbling engine into a roar several times, he put the floor shift into first gear and eased out the clutch. The old, green truck sped forward. Sean gripped the thick, black steering wheel with both hands, letting out a "Ya—hoo!"

We were headed for Main Street. Luckily, Sean decided to drive the side streets for practice. He tried turning to the right at the first corner, but the steering wheel wouldn't budge. Panic struck as the veins in his forearms bulged. We made the corner after the truck jumped up on the opposite curb, trimmed a hedge and just missed a power pole.

Grease came to both of our minds as a possible cure for this arthritic steering system. I tried to act calm as I caught my breath and clamped on to the door handle, preparing to eject if Sean started to traverse another intersection. Somehow, we made it the five blocks to Sean's house.

The next morning from a half a block away, I saw Sean's big, red sneakers sticking out from under the rear of the old truck.

"Mike, the shaft is clanging and ready to drop," he informed me. I knelt down and saw a handful of u-joint parts laying next to Sean's shoulder. His face was spotted alternately with freckles and grease. I had done my share of mechanicking lately, since I also had an old '52 Chevy panel truck. I was always good for advice, and Sean obviously believed I knew a lot more than I did.

"This u-joint is shot," he continued. After handing me several rough-looking parts, he said discouragingly, "I can't afford any new parts till next week."

I only wanted to be supportive. "Sean, it will hold up for awhile; just get something sticky from the house, like honey or toothpaste. We need to repack it so the needle bearings stay in line while you cinch it down."

Sean wiggled out from under the pickup, quickly wiped the spots across his face and jogged into the kitchen.

Sean crawled back under the truck to join me. He had returned with a large tube of Colgate toothpaste. "I prefer Pepsodent," I joked, as he squeezed a wad of bright, white dental scrub onto the bearing cup. I held the shaft up as Sean tightened the u-joint keepers. He was obviously relieved to have the truck back together. I didn't dare tell him that toothpaste was an original and strictly experimental idea. If it worked, I planned to apply for a patent.

I hoped Sean didn't mention it to anyone.

The registration hadn't arrived, so Sean had a few days to go over the rig. He pulled a leaf out of the rear springs to make less weight on the front end for easier steering.

I went to visit friends in eastern Montana. After several days I called Sean. When he realized it was me all he could say in a loud, almost hysterical voice was, "Toothpaste!...TOOTHPASTE!"

Oh no. Something didn't sound good.

"I thought you were my friend, Mike," Sean moaned. "I was taking Jan (his girlfriend) out on a Sunday ride. Seven miles east of town there was a click, click, then a loud bang. The drive shaft shot out from under the truck and stuck into a wheat field like a javelin thrower had flung it. We pushed the heavy old beast over to the side. Finally a tow truck pulled up."

Sean explained in detail to the truck driver how he had just repacked the u-joint with toothpaste. The driver stared at him, wrinkled his brow, glanced around to see if this was "Candid Camera," and questioned Sean cautiously.

"Toothpaste?"

"Yea, toothpaste." Sean was catching on to how ridiculous this sounded. He hoped the gent wouldn't ask again.

"Toothpaste!" he burst out. "In all my years...."

Sean was ready to kill.

Lucky for me, I was in eastern Montana.

Relatives

In the moving business you are valued by how much you can lift and how little damage is done in the process. Pianos, freezers and dining room tables are for the pro's. Squashy is a pro.

He has moved every piano in New York City at least once, along with every other freezer on the East Coast.

His father, known as Big Squash, was a lifetime mover. Big Squash wasn't very tall either. They worked together when little Squashy graduated from high school. Back then the story was if you wanted to move the Brooklyn Bridge, "Just put a Squash under each end, and tell them where you want it."

After Big Squash retired, Squashy had run the gauntlet of moving partners—big, strong, dumb ones who could lift anything, then destroy a house trying to find their way to the truck; and the smaller, often intelligent guys who never left a scratch, but could only lift a kitchen chair and seemed to spend all day planning their next move.

Whenever possible, Squashy learned to work alone.

Early one sunny June morning, as the long-timers sat drinking their coffee outside the dispatcher's office, Mr. McShane, the boss, poked his head out and yelled, "Hey, Squashy!"

"Oh no. He wants me to move another safe. I hope they remembered to unload it this time," he thought, as he wiped the hard roll seeds off his pants.

"Squash, this is my nephew Teddy," McShane continued. "He's on vacation from Cornell University, and I want you to break him in for a couple of days." Squashy shook hands. Teddy reminded him of Maynard G. Krebbs from the "Dobie Gillis Show."

"I hope he's stronger than he looks," Squashy thought.

That day was a simple job, a small apartment five stories up, overlooking a hedge-lined courtyard.

From taking the bunk beds apart with Teddy, Squashy knew it was going to be a long initiation. Teddy stood back making suggestions while Squashy dismantled and carefully stacked the boards against the bedroom wall. By mid-morning Squashy was wishing the boss had sent Teddy to camp. He was making conversation with the customers and their teenage daughter, which was fine, except it slowed the family down.

The last thing needed when trying to move a household is the family in the middle.

When they finally left, Squashy had had enough advice for one day.

He encouraged Teddy into the freight elevator, advising him to get as close to the back wall as possible while mattresses and bed springs were stacked inside. Squashy hesitated, then continued to pin Teddy to the back wall of the tightly stuffed elevator.

As Squashy rode the other elevator down, he enjoyed the quiet. He stepped out into the first floor lobby. The freight elevator was a bit slower. The bell rang, the door rolled open, and Squashy grabbed the first mattress. Then without hesitating a second, he reached over and hit the 21st floor button on the inside control panel.

The doors shut and up it went—Teddy and the mattresses all the way to the 21st floor.

Squashy chuckled as he walked to the van. Then he explained to Louie, who was loading the truck, how he had just packed Teddy into the freight elevator and sent him on tour.

"Good!" Louie blurted. "That college professor has been down here telling me how to load this stuff."

"How long have I been packing vans?" Louie put his hands out, palms up, and shrugged his shoulders. "We can teach him something he won't learn at Corny College."

Squashy headed inside. The freight elevator doors were just beginning to open. He almost yelled, "Where did you go, Ted?" Instead, he reached in and hit the 25th floor button. The quiet was just too precious.

Squashy knew this could be his last day on the job. Two more trips and he met Teddy's delayed express load at the first floor. "Where did you go?" Squashy asked nonchalantly as a spooked, blanched-looking Teddy leapt out over the last mattress, looking like a cat that had just fallen in a bird bath.

Teddy didn't talk much on the afternoon job. He had learned one of the first lessons in moving.

Danny

When I first laid eyes on Danny I knew he was dead. It was 5:30 in the morning; under the dim street light he lay next to the yellow line on Route 2. I put my bike down on the curb, then crept toward him. He was curled up, his blond hair matted and blood crusted. Afraid to touch him, I lay flat on the cold asphalt a foot away, waiting to see any movement.

His back rose slightly. I lay quiet, hoping I hadn't imagined it. Then he gave a weak cough, more like a distant whimper. His head moved slowly. He uncurled, and a glazed eye stared through me. The other eye hung by a thin cord on his cheek. Time seemed to stand still. I hoped he could read my mind: I only wanted to help.

I had never seen a raccoon this close.

Carefully, I wrapped my jean jacket around the big coon. He groaned and gurgled as I slowly lifted and carried him into the nearest yard where I laid him in the dew-tipped grass. Leaving my coat on the wounded coon, I jumped back on the bike to finish the newspaper deliveries. Peddling as fast as I could, my imagination ran wild while I tried to remember the houses that subscribed to the paper. I was doing the route as a favor for the friends I was visiting in Needham, Massachusetts. It was a vacation for me to be out of New York and to stay a few weeks on a small farm in the country.

The early morning sun crested the eastern horizon as I returned to my new friend. He was still faintly breathing. I padded the big coon in the front basket with my coat.

I kept whispering, "Danny, Danny." It seemed like a good name for a raccoon. His good eye opened slowly. I tried to control my excitement by pedaling slowly and avoiding bumps. It was beyond my wildest dreams to have an animal to take care of.

As we rolled into the barnyard, Danny instantly became the center of attention. Kids of all sizes formed a circle around us. Danny couldn't straighten out. He would try to walk, going in a slow circle, then fall over, lie there, get up and try again. His front paws looked like human baby hands with short, black fingers and tiny fingernails. He gripped the grass, pulling up his large, oval body. His two hind feet looked more like my grandpa's—long, bony and wrinkled. The left one was useless. It just dragged behind as he hopped on the right foot.

Warm Jell-O mix through an eyedropper was the only food I could get him to eat. Sleep and rest seemed to be the main medicine. In two days Danny's good eye was clearer. He seemed glad to see me each morning and would give a cluck, cluck, cackle when I rubbed his head. The eye on his cheek was drying out, looking more like a raisin now. I was afraid to touch it and hoped it might fall off like my new little sister's umbilical cord.

For exercise, Danny leaned against a table leg and walked in a circle. I guessed his back or hip was broken.

It was time to return home to New York. Summer vacation was over, and my break in the country was up. I stuffed my small backpack, made a sign "N.Y.C.", picked up Danny and hoofed it for Route 128.

Six hours and several rides later we were dropped off on the Cross Bronx Expressway.

Danny sat next to my pack, tucking his head each time a large semitrailer truck blew by. We got lots of looks. Cars slowed, but it took awhile to get a ride. Finally a flashy, long limousine stopped. I loaded Danny and my pack onto the back seat and hopped up front next to a tall, classy-dressed black man. He smiled, showing two gold teeth.

"What kind of a critter is that?" he asked with a suspicious look.

I said, "It's a hurt raccoon," hoping the word *hurt* would help.

The man stared.

It was obvious this city slicker had never seen a raccoon. I turned to look at Danny who was almost standing on my pack, glaring back with that one good eye at our new friend.

The man turned to me and said, "I never had no wild animals in this limo," as though he were afraid. I tried to sound encouraging and said, "Danny is my pet. He got run over."

He put the gear shift in drive and screeched the wheels as we rolled off the curb and onto the busy four-lane highway.

The Cross Bronx is full of holes. Each time the car bumped, Danny cackled a bit and the driver jerked his head around to glance at the raccoon. The limo swerved lane-to-lane. Within two miles the driver was sweating. Wiping his brow, he very apologetically said, "I'm sorry, son, I just can't drive with no wild animal glaring at my jugular vein and growling in the back seat."

There we stood on the curb once again, a little closer to home.

After several more rides, Danny and I were at our front stoop. After a round of hugs, I picked Danny up to introduce him to my Mom and sisters. They all jumped back. I told them the story of finding my friend injured on the road. Mom stood her distance and said, "Well, I guess it could have been a horse or a bear." That made it clear to me that I could keep Danny, at least until he recovered.

The next morning Danny and I headed down Northern Boulevard for the nearest animal doctor. I'd never been in the clinic before. But I was sure the doctor would be as excited as I was about taking care of a wild animal, especially after all the poodles and cats he had to see in this neighborhood. With Danny in my arms, I strode into the front office as proud as if I had just saved the last member of an endangered species.

When I sat Danny on the front desk, the woman stood up fast. She talked to me from a distance, looking like she might leap for the fire exit if I came any closer. Before I could explain our predicament, she hurried down the hall and returned with a big man dressed in a white Dr. Kildare shirt. I introduced myself, as the doctor quickly rolled Danny over on his side and said, "I can't do anything for that animal except put him to sleep." He said it so matter-of-factly I was stunned. I had thought if anyone would value Danny, it would be someone who cared for animals. I knew how far Danny had come in the week since I found him. No one was going to tell me that he wasn't going to make it. I couldn't respond. The doctor shrugged his shoulders, then walked off down the hall.

Danny seemed glad to be back in my arms. As I headed for the heavy steel door, I looked into the waiting room. There were two women in long, fur coats; each had a small poodle on her lap. One dog wore a diamond-studded collar. There was a big Siamese cat peering from a cage.

I turned. Danny and I went in and took a seat across from the decked-out women. Danny looked up and cackled. All hell broke loose. The poodles tried to hide under their owners' coats as the cat let out a death wail.

The doctor arrived in seconds with the receptionist right behind him. "I told you I can't do anything for that animal," he said. One women tucked her FiFi under her arm and clicked her high heels loudly as she strutted past the doctor and out the door. He was turning red now and looked as if he would like to put both me and Danny to sleep.

"You're the doctor," I said. "You could help Danny if you wanted to." That would be my last try. He went from red to purple, then held the door open as he said, all tight-lipped and angry, "Bring that raccoon." I followed the doctor to a small room. First he snipped the cord and threw Danny's dried-up eye into the garbage can. We then wrapped a thick leather blanket around Danny, leaving only his bad hip exposed. The doctor filled a syringe the size of a small baby bottle and attached a needle the length of a railroad spike. I held Danny with all my might as the doctor approached him. The shot seemed to hurt me more than my raccoon friend.

I promised Dr. Goodman he would not see me again and thanked him as he escorted Danny and me to the front door.

Danny became the talk of the neighborhood. After school there was often a small audience staring through the windows of the small porch we fixed up for him. Danny washed everything before eating. He would finger and scrub every cranny, often sniff, and then scrub again. I told Mom he would soon be able to pitch in and earn his keep by doing the dishes. She glared at me as if to say, "You've been out in the country way to long," but after watching Danny's washing routine, I swear I saw a nod of agreement.

Marshmallows were Danny's favorite treat. When he saw me coming with a bag, he would jump up and wave his front paws as if to beg, then grab the marshmallow with both paws and waddle as fast as he could for the wash bucket. The first time Danny washed a marshmallow his expression became one of panic. His prize became sticky as he dipped and scrubbed. It then turned into a one-coon taffy-pulling contest, with Danny cackling louder and louder as if to say, "I give up. Now please let go."

I hated the thought and tried to block it from my mind, but after several weeks it was obvious that Danny was ready to go back to the woods. Early one fall morning, I lifted him into my bike basket. Danny sat up, gripping the front rim with his long narrow fingers. As I pedaled, the cool breeze on his face made it look as though he were smiling. I was trying to be happy for him, but it was hard to override my own feelings.

I finally decided on the place, next to a small stream on the Whitney estate. I lifted Danny from the basket and placed him in the damp grass. I talked as I petted him; he played with my fingers. Then he looked up with that one, shiny black eye. I felt him say thanks. Things got cloudy for me as tears flooded my vision. I stood up and told Danny how lucky he was because he could go play in the woods and I had to go to school.

As I walked my bike back to the road, I stopped to look back several times. The last time, he was gone.

A Friend

Andrew knew the Holy Mass backwards and had built an altar of wooden milk crates in his bedroom.

Many evenings he dressed his brother Kevin and me in his large, altar-boy cassocks. Andrew wrapped a colorful curtain over his broad shoulders, lit the candles and then, using grape juice for wine and sugar wafers as the Host, he practiced saying Mass.

Correcting our Latin, he often reminded us that this wasn't for fun.

Kevin and I were eight. Andrew at twelve had the build of a professional football player. It was easy to recognize Andrew's walk. He strode by our apartment window each morning on his three-mile hike to assist the priest with 7:00 a.m. Mass. Mom often tapped on the window, and Andrew flashed his wide smile and waved.

Then she would say, "There goes Saint Andrew."

His father died when Andrew was nine. Then he, his Mom, three brothers and a sister lived in the first row of the housing projects.

Many kids from the apartments attended Saint Mary's, a Catholic school perched on Manhasset Hill. Boys had to wear a suit and tie beginning in first grade, which we all fought daily, all except Andrew. His suit was without a wrinkle, and his tie snugged up to a stiff, white shirt collar.

Each day after school I tried to keep up with him on the walk home, asking questions like, "Andrew, how come you don't take your tie off? School's over." He would hit me with that smile. I was sure he knew something I didn't. He rushed to get home to deliver newspapers.

Often he talked about his cousin Bobby, a Franciscan missionary in Boliva, who worked with people who were starving or dying from lack of medicine. Andrew would point to his black, shiny shoes and say, "Most of them don't even have a pair of shoes."

Andrew's voice changed when he talked about his cousin, and often I'd swear I could see one of the biggest, toughest guys in the projects fighting back tears. There was little question who Andrew's hero was.

I looked forward to our walks home after school. It wasn't long before I had a paper route and was on the altar assisting with Mass.

Andrew's dream came true: He was accepted into Saint Joseph's Monastery in upstate New York. We all hated to see him go, but we knew he was destined for the priesthood.

Six months later, Andrew was back. Now attending public school, he still wore the suit and tie. At noon he spent his lunch hour teaching gym at St. Mary's Elementary School.

Mom said it was reading and math grades that kept Andrew out of the seminary. I could understand since all of us from the projects had a hard time with grades, but Andrew's enthusiasm should have been enough to convince them of his devotion.

I was glad Andrew was back. He had been missed by everyone. He dropped by often in his small, red sports car.

On Christmas Eve Santa arrived at the front door. Our youngest sister Susan was asleep. Santa went up and kneeled at her bedside with his hand lightly on her shoulder. Susan rubbed her eyes, trying to focus. Then Santa and she had a long conversation as the rest of us stacked our heads in the hall trying to listen.

He finished with, "I know you've been a good girl. I watched you helping your Mom." He pulled a doll out of his black duffle bag and handed it to her. Susan was bubbling. She begged Santa to stay. He said he had lots of kids to see, and off he went.

The front door was barely closed when Susan flew downstairs. We were all sitting next to the lit tree. She ran into the living room, waving her doll. She repeated over and over how Santa had visited and talked with her; she had the new doll as evidence.

After a knock at the door, in came Andrew dressed for midnight Mass. Susan ran to him, telling her story. Andrew grinned and shared in her excitment.

Santa had made Susan feel really special.

It was 1966, and the draft was on. Mom cried most of the day. She told us Andrew was going to war. "Mom, he's tough," was all I could say. He now had a wife Sandy and was soon to be a father.

Andrew sent cards and gifts from Viet Nam. It seemed like forever until he was home for R&R.

Sandy and their newborn Michelle were staying with us the night he arrived. Andrew looked bigger and better than ever. Dumping his shoulder bag, he gave Sandy a bear hug then raced up the stairs to see his daughter for the first time.

Holding the infant to his chest, he rocked side to side over her crib in the dark.

Mom scooted us downstairs. Andrew was crying. I didn't understand. Mom said he was crying because he was happy. I didn't know men could cry. It was like seeing your own father fall apart.

The days flew by. Andrew didn't talk about what life in Nam was like. It was December and cold in New York, with two days remaining until Andrew had to leave again.

He asked if I knew of any good ice. We found a pond on a golf course. We climbed the barbed wire fence and skated past midnight. Andrew could skate like a pro. Several times I stopped and watched him spin and jump in the soft moonlight. He was so big and powerful, yet so graceful on ice.

We stopped several times and talked about how lucky we all were as kids in the projects, like one big family. When he talked about his new daughter Michelle, I saw his chest puff up in the dim light. Andrew seemed to have a lot on his mind, but never mentioned leaving.

We got in late. Everyone was sleeping. I lay awake, thinking that my adopted big brother was now a man, a soldier, a father. How different things often work out.

Back to Nam he went.

We counted the weeks until Andrew would be home for good. Mom scratched them off the calendar. Three weeks left. It was spring in New York. The trees blossomed. The sun was still up after dinner.

We were all at the table the evening our sister Mimi came screaming hysterically through the front door. She had been cleaning tables for the priest at the rectory across the street when a call had come for Monsignor Sharp. Mimi overheard him tell another priest, "We need to make arrangements for Andrew Bukovinsky." When we were able to understand what she was trying to tell us, everything stopped for days.

Finally I got my legs to carry me up next to the casket. Andrew was dressed in full uniform. He looked like a king with all the medals pinned to his big chest.

I stood a long time not wanting to say good-bye. Then I swear I saw a trace of that wide smile, that smile that not so long ago had told me that he knew something I didn't. I blessed myself and saluted the Friend, Brother, Father, and Saint we had just lost.

Fifteen years later I tried to name my newborn son Andrew. I couldn't do it.

As Mom had often said, "There's only one Andrew."

Glossary

ALASKA - Largest state in the U.S., separated from Russia by the Bering Strait. Bordered by British Columbia and Yukon Territory   586,000 sq miles; Pop. 302,000

ALCAN - Alaska Highway, runs 1520 miles from Dawson Creek, B.C. Canada to Fairbanks. Built during WWII, much improved over the last ten years.

ANCHORAGE - Alaskas largest city -began in 1915 as a tent city to build the Alaska railroad - Pop. 200,000.

ATHABASCAN - A major Alaskan Indian group - nomadic hunters originally -most now live in the Interior in permanent villages on the banks of the Yukon and Koyukuk Rivers.

AURORA BOREALIS (Northern Lights) - Luminous bands of light, occasionally appearing in the northern night sky. Some claim to hear the lights cracking on clear cold nights and that they are actually the spirits of the deceased and can be whistled down to just above your head.

BABICHE - Long strings of rawhide used to weave snowshoes and tie dogsleds together. Mostly made from caribou skin.

BARREL STOVE - Wood burning stove built from a 55 gallon fuel drum. Used mostly in rural Alaska where drums are often plentiful.

BOOTIES - Small boots made of canvas or cordora to protect sled dogs' feet from sharp icy trails - usally held on with a velcro strap to save time. Thousands of such booties are used each year on the Iditarod dog race.

BUSH - Rural Alaska - most of the state, not connected by road- accessible by airplane or boat.

CABIN FEVER - Malady that grips many Alaskans (mid winter) from lack of sun, intense cold and confinement in small cabins. Only known cure is to head for the Travel Agents' office.

CACHE (kash) Small shed often on stilts used to store food and supplies out of reach of animals.

CARIBOU - Alaska's indigenous reindeer - smaller then moose; both sexes grow large antlers -they cluster in large herds across the state.

ESKIMO - One of Alaska's three major native groups. They live predominantly on the coast. A tough, hardworking cheerful people they still live a mostly subsistence lifestyle.

FAIRBANKS - AK's 2nd largest city - at the end of the Alcan. Established: 1903. POP. Now 75,000. It's considered the capital of the interior.

FISHWHEEL - Resembles a paddle wheel with wire baskets that scoop fish from the rivers. This contraption is anchored to the shore and spins using the rivers current. Many line the banks near the villages on the Yukon when the salmon are running.

GANGLINE - Also called a towline, the main line from a dogsled to the lead dog to which other team members are attached by clips.

GEE - Command to leader to take dogteam to the right.

GRIZZLY - Another name for brown bear, large, often blond or silver tipped hair, highly feared and respected in Alaska.

HAW - Command to lead dog for turning the team to the left.

HOMESTEAD - Land acquired from the government through sweat equity, usually 160 acres - you had to prove up, build a cabin and plant a small section of the land.

HUSKY - Wolf-like dog popular in Alaska for pulling sleds, smaller than Malemutes but wiry and powerful, enduring animals, often very loyal and anxious to pull.

ICE FOG - Occurs at sub zero tempatures along oceans and river fronts, also in Fairbanks due to auto and chimney emissions at low temperatures. Visibility can be zero zero.

IDITAROD - Annual 1,000 plus mile dog sled race from Anchorage to Nome, which has become known as the Last Great Race. A spectacular event each March in Alaska.

KAYAK - A narrow boat pointed at both ends, propelled by a single oar with paddles on both ends. Developed by the Eskimos to hunt sea mammals.

KOTZEBUE - Large Eskimo village in N. W. Alaska, north of the Artic circle. Pop. 2000.

McKINLEY - North America's tallest mountain at 20,320 feet, a very popular climbing attraction.

MELOZITNA - Small river draining into the Yukon just upriver from the village of Ruby from the North.

MOOSE - The largest of the deer family weighing 800-1600 lbs. found throughout Alaska.

MUKLUK - Knee high mocassins made by natives of skins and canvas with leather bottoms, they are light flexible and warm.

MUSHER - The driver of a dog team.

NENANA - Small town on the Tanana river 55 miles from Fairbanks; mostly Athabascan.

NOME - The largest village on Norten Sound, site of one of Alaska's major gold discovery in 1889.

POTLATCH - Native ceremony held to commemorate a particular event, often a funeral where relatives and friends gather for feasting, story telling and dancing.

SNO-GO - Another name for snow machine or ski-doo.

SOURDOUGH - A yeast, flour and water mix to make bread. An Alaskan who is sour on the country but doesn't have enough dough to leave.

TANANA - Small Athabascan village at the confluence of the Tanana and Yukon River. Pop. 400. Sled dogs: 750.

TOZITNA - Small river runs into the Yukon 10 miles down river from Tanana. Homesteaders staked ground 40 miles up at the Bluffs. Stan and Helen, Russ and Ann were some of the first.

TUNDRA - Treeless expanse covering much of Alaska. It is easier to travel on during the winter.

YUKON - 2,300 mile long river; largest and longest in Alaska. It starts in Canada and crosses Alaska into the Bering Sea; many small villages set on the banks of this mighty river. It was the highway of the interior during the Gold Rush and still today many colorful characters drift down it.